Flight into History

The WRIGHT BROTHERS
and the AIR AGE

Flight into History

The WRIGHT BROTHERS and the AIR AGE

By ELSBETH E. FREUDENTHAL

NORMAN
UNIVERSITY OF OKLAHOMA PRESS
1949

By ELSBETH E. FREUDENTHAL

The Aviation Business: from Kitty Hawk to Wall Street
(New York, 1940)

Flight into History: The Wright Brothers and the Air Age
(Norman, 1949)

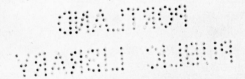

WILBUR AND ORVILLE WRIGHT are known to some as "the inventors of the aeroplane;"[1] to others as "the first men to fly an airplane." According to some experts these claims rob other pioneers of their rightful place in history. Claimants to the title of "first to fly" include the famous Brazilian Alberto Santos-Dumont, the Americans James J. Montgomery of California, Augustus M. Herring, and Hiram S. Maxim, and the French Clement Ader, as well as many others. All of these, and the many other pioneers for whom similar claims are put forth, made their own, unique contributions to the history of aeronautics.

For arguments about the title of "first" muddy the waters and serve no purpose. This is particularly true of the Wright brothers, who were never a clear-cut black or white, but possessed many shadings. They themselves used qualifying phrases frequently and with caution chose exact words to define exact meanings, often stating the facts they did not mean as well as those they did. Their meanings, as well as their motives, were often obscured as a consequence of these qualifications.

Clear-cut labels, trying to state in a few words a complicated accomplishment, obscure the true contributions of the Wrights. Whether they were the first to rise from the ground —and it seems true that they were not—is an inaccurate gauge of their achievement. It appears indubitable that they were the first to demonstrate controlled mechanical flight.

[1] In keeping with the spelling of the period covered by this book, "aeroplane," rather than the now more common "airplane," is used.

Much more important was their role of midwives to the business of flying. It was the Wright brothers who, as businessmen, insisted on making the science and theory of aeronautics into a paying business. They themselves did not realize their role, for their emphasis was on their claims of being scientists whose inventions had enabled them to fly first. They were, actually, practical businessmen, seeking a return on their investments of much time and small amounts of money, and it shocked them to think that success could not result in money.

Their first flights, on that famous seventeenth of December, 1903, marked the beginning of heavier-than-air flying. Their success was not achieved overnight or by chance, nor was it a surprise to those few who knew of their careful work of preparation. In this work they had been helped beyond measure by the prior efforts of hundreds of other men. So much work had preceded theirs that December 17, 1903, marked the grand climax of centuries of thought about flying.

The theory of aeronautics was an old one by 1896, when the Wrights first began to study it. Indeed, practical flight in a heavier-than-air machine was actually just around the corner. The great mass of theoretical data, accumulated through decades, was waiting for practical application. The single elements were all available: Penaud and Gauchot's patents, Wenham's biplane surfaces, Maxim's patents, Hargrave's box kite, Langley's powered models, Chanute's adaptation of the Pratt truss—all these, and many more, offered a wealth of material from which to choose. Through lighter-than-air craft, men had assaulted the heavens for over one hundred years before the Wrights were born. The gasoline engine, essential for the airplane, finally had been developed.

It is inevitable that all successful "firsts" are claimed by more than one person, and, indeed, they frequently occur simultaneously. In the history of the aeroplane, however, claims rivaling those of the Wrights were facilitated by the brothers' unwillingness to make a public demonstration of their plane after the first flights of 1903. They did not, for five long years thereafter—until 1908—make any flights before the public eye. And then their first completely public flight occurred, not in the United States but in France.

During these five years enormous progress in flying was made by other men, while discussions about the mysterious Wrights raged over the world. But the brothers refused to make flights for the public to see; they would not enter competitions, nor would they publish details of the construction of their machine. Having issued one statement about their 1903 flights, for two years they confined their few statements to saying what they could do, not what they had accomplished. And in general they tried to keep as aloof as possible from the arguments about them.

The chief reason for believing their claims in this period was the word of Octave Chanute, foremost American authority, that he had actually seen them fly, and that he believed their assertions to be completely truthful. Chanute was one of the Wrights' few intimate friends, and their friendship spanned the first decade of this century—a period of intense activity culminating in world-wide fame for the brothers and of great significance in the development of the aeroplane.

Since Chanute, through his writings as well as his experiments, was an acknowledged authority on aeronautics, his role as confidant of the Wrights was most important. Through him, moreover, the brothers came in contact with the whole world of aeronautical thought, for Chanute corresponded with aeronautical inventors of all countries.

The Wrights, either through shyness or lack of social grace, usually avoided public knowledge of their private lives. But Chanute they admitted to their circle of a few chosen friends. On his side, Chanute showed interest in their efforts and thoughts and affection for their characters. From 1900 to 1906, years which the Wrights felt were their most important productive period, the relationship with Chanute was a close one.

From 1906 to 1910, as other attempts to fly became successful and the field of flying spread open like a fan, so the paths of Chanute and the Wrights diverged.

As the contribution of the Wright brothers was made in this decade, from 1900 to 1910, an understanding of their role implies a knowledge of their relationship with Chanute. For in these ten years the aeroplane emerged from its hundreds of years of slow development in secluded laboratories and studies, into a full-sized mechanism that actually flew. The Wrights' efforts, starting in 1900, helped to push open the doors behind which the aeroplane was forming, almost ready to fly.

Having developed their powered plane, the Wrights flew it successfully, and kept it under control while in flight.

Then they were faced with the problem of making money. Sensing the growth of business into big units which typified this first decade of the twentieth century in America, they found the answer to their problem by starting the aviation industry so that it could take its place in American business life. By 1910 the Wright brothers had pioneered in making aviation a paying business.

ELSBETH E. FREUDENTHAL

New York City
February 10, 1949

FOR THE HELP AND ENCOURAGEMENT of my friends in writing this book I am deeply grateful.

I am indebted also to the public libraries throughout the country, whose treasure houses of information have been available at all times, and whose courtesies to students are unlimited. Libraries which have been especially helpful include: Library of Congress; Library of the Institute of the Aeronautical Sciences, Inc.; The New York Public Library (and in particular its Economics Division); the Public Library, Denver; and the Supreme Court Law Library of New Mexico.

Several members of The Early Birds, an organization of those who flew before 1916, lent me their collections of aeronautical material and inspired me with their knowledge of this period.

Many of the illustrations used are by courtesy of the United States Signal Corps.

CONTENTS

ILLUSTRATIONS

Flight into History

The WRIGHT BROTHERS
and the AIR AGE

CHAPTER I

Two Bicycle Makers

ONE DAY in 1900, Octave Chanute, well-known railroad engineer, bridge builder, and authority on aeronautics, living in Chicago, received a letter postmarked Dayton, Ohio, from a bicycle maker.[1] Possibly it was from two men—brothers—for it was difficult to determine, then as later, whether Wilbur Wright was writing for himself only, or was including also his brother Orville.

This letter marked the throwing of the Wright brothers' hat into the ring of aeronautical endeavor. It was almost a formal entry into a contest, for Chanute, three years before, had invited men to come forward with suggestions for "improving our gliding practice." When Chanute issued this invitation, he was already the greatest authority on aeronautics in America, and foremost in the world. By writing to him, therefore, the Wrights showed that they were sufficiently sure of themselves, after several years of thought and study, to feel justified in taking up the time of this great man.

Chanute, always responsive to any appeal for help from a serious student of aeronautics, answered Wilbur's letter fully, recognizing his serious purpose, and thus gladly took up the roles of mentor, guide, and father-confessor to these young men. The Wrights continued for several years to ask his advice and counsel, and hundreds of letters were exchanged which included arguments about technical points of theory, invitations to Chanute to visit them, and telegraphic appeals for him to help them out at business conferences.

[1] Octave Chanute, "A History of the Wright Flying Experiments," *Scientific American* Supplement No. 1639 (June 1, 1907), 26262.

The correspondence continued from 1900 to 1910 between Chanute, "The Father of American Aviation," and the Wright brothers, builders and pilots of the first practical flying machine.

When Wilbur first wrote to Chanute, he was already a man of thirty-three years and Orville was four years younger. The brothers were thus mature adults, as well as established businessmen, at the time they began their active careers in aeronautics. Their characters were no longer fluid, but were already formed by the circumstances of their youth and their previous business ventures.

Three years after this inauguration of their active work, the Wright brothers, bicycle makers of Dayton, made the first controlled flights in a powered flying machine in the history of the world. Although several years elapsed before their achievements were generally conceded, by the end of 1908 they had proved to the world that their machine and their abilities as pilots could meet any challenge.

What kind of men were these two brothers who rose from obscure positions in a middle western town to fame that circled the world? What made it possible for them to carve a niche for their names in the history of mankind?

Few facts are known about the Wrights' lives before they became famous, and these few serve only to tease the imagination further about the miracle of creative ability. For it is a source of wonder to each student of history that the inheritors of centuries of thought and experimentation in aeronautics should have been these two quiet, reserved owners of a bicycle shop, who possessed little formal education and no technical training.[2]

There is little in the Wrights' early youth to indicate unusual ability or their future importance. It is indeed fascinat-

[2] An excellent account of this period can be found in *The Wright Brothers*, by Fred C. Kelly, 5–15.

4

'ing to see them grow into the part for which they are now famous, to watch their plans mature, and to observe how they gradually carved out for themselves the honored title of being the first to demonstrate controlled flight in a heavier-than-air machine.

Wilbur was born near Richmond, Indiana, in 1867. From the time of Orville's birth in 1871 the Wrights lived continuously in Dayton, Ohio. Their lives were typical of many boys born in the eighteen eighties into that respectable middle class in which the family was often pressed for money but never suffered actual need or want. Their family life was of primary importance to the brothers. All their actions in later years showed a carrying out of early training and habits and thoughts, never a breaking away from them. In the midst of his greatest fame—in France in 1908—Wilbur was homesick and yearned for a bicycle ride in his own country. Indeed, as their renown increased, the brothers clung more tenaciously to their home and their Dayton environment; they refused resolutely ever to take on any of the attributes and characteristics of citizens of the world. Because of their rigid training, which included strict observance of Sundays and total abstinence from liquor and smoking, there was never a possibility that they would become, or would want to become, men of the world.

Of their mother, Susan Catherine Koerner Wright, little is known. She is said to have had a college education and to have been the best mathematician in her class. Since Wilbur was twenty-two years old and Orville was eighteen when she died (in 1889), she must have exercised great influence in the home.[3]

Their father, Milton, was without doubt always an important factor in their lives, his death occurring after Wilbur's. At the time of Orville's birth, in 1871, Mr. Wright was the

[3] Heinrich Adams, *Flug,* 66; Alfred L. H. Hildebrandt, *Die Brüder Wright,* 8; M. G. and E. L. Webb, *Famous Living Americans,* 571.

editor of the *Religious Telescope,* official organ of the church of the United Brethren in Christ. Later he became a bishop in this sect, but his elevation did not, on the evidence available, noticeably improve the financial resources of the family.

Other members of the family were two brothers, Reuchlin and Lorin, and a sister, Katharine, the youngest, born three years after Orville. Reuchlin Wright lived in Kansas for most of his life, and Lorin's role in the lives of his younger brothers seems to have been a minor one. It was reported that when Wilbur was asked about his older brothers, in France many years later, he "made a vague gesture and said, briefly and disdainfully, 'The others—they are married!' "[4]

For Katharine, who did not commit this indiscretion of marriage until many years after Wilbur's death, the brothers had a deep affection. Her role in their lives was always behind the scenes, but through her great interest and attachment for her brothers, she exerted an important influence on them.

There is every evidence that the Wrights' home life was pleasant and equable, with a notable absence of bickering and animosities. Their congeniality with each other, reinforced by their natural shyness and reserve (which they never lost), all combined to limit their relationships outside their home. Possibly their restricted financial means, which caused them to become wage earners early in life, was another explanation for their lack of many social contacts. The important fact is that they made few friends and indulged even fewer intimacies. Their house, as preserved in Henry Ford's hysterical agglomeration of Americana, shows a comfortable home, with less emphasis on the esthetic than on the conventional.

Wilbur and Orville both left school when quite young, in spite of the fact that their mother, their older brothers, and Katharine all attended college.[5] This has been attributed to the family's finances. The brothers' great carefulness in money

[4] François Peyrey, *Les Oiseaux Artificiels,* 196.
[5] Archibald Henderson, *Contemporary Immortals,* 139.

matters throughout their lives, their rigid balancing of budgets so that they would not spend more on aeronautics than they had planned, and their unwillingness to borrow money in order to develop their flying machines—all these qualities may have come from their youth, when they began to support themselves. Wilbur left school when he was only thirteen or fourteen years old, and always worked thereafter. Orville went on to high school, but he, too, early found ways of earning money.

There are indications that their father's career as a bishop was not a peaceful one. Several times their experiments were interrupted while the brothers settled the various troubles in their father's church. Even earlier there had been difficulties in the church, which laid the groundwork for the Wrights' attitude toward the press—an almost eccentric indifference. This unconcern was attributed by Wilbur to the fact that the grievances of the dissident members against his father had been aired fully in the newspapers, and that his father had remained unmoved by these attacks. As quoted by a later biographer, Wilbur explained the situation as follows: "As Superintendent, my father for many years supervised the clergymen. Therefore it was necessary now and then to remove the unfit elements from the service of the church. Then these people attacked my father in the newspapers. However, he did not concern himself with this. And so as young boys we learned not to pay any attention to newspaper talk."[6]

Another aspect of their father's life which undoubtedly influenced the boys was his interest in scientific matters. Described as a poor clergyman with scientific tastes, he is said to have invented a typewriter. Unlike his sons, whose ability to concentrate on and develop an idea into a practical object was their most notable quality, the father did not develop his typewriter. But his interest in mechanics thus evidenced was important.

[6] Adams, *Flug,* 71.

7

In view of the brothers' later hostility to the press (their refusal to give interviews or to admit journalists as witnesses to their experiments) and also their reluctance to write accounts of their work, it is interesting to note that they themselves had had some experience in journalism. Orville, while still in high school, started with Wilbur's help to write, print, and distribute a small magazine. The printing was done on a handmade printing press, constructed almost entirely by the boys themselves. They published, at various times from 1889 on, weeklies called *The Midget, The Evening Item, The West Side News, Snap-Shots,* and *The Tattler*.[7] That they believed these ventures were important was shown when Wilbur said many years later, "I have found in my experience as a newspaper man ...." Indeed, Wilbur's many letters to Chanute and the occasional articles written by the brothers all show a good command of language.

Most important was the fact that from the beginning they worked independently. The evidence available indicates that neither Wilbur nor Orville ever worked for any other person, and that they never had the experiences of applying for or holding a job. Working for and by themselves, they developed the characteristics often shown by independent workers—the ability to plan a project and to carry it out. Used to being independent of others' opinions, ways of working, and standards, they had only their own standards to meet. Since they were serious young men, they set these standards high. The resulting qualities—determination to work alone and unaided by others and resoluteness in carrying out their own plans—were later to be responsible for their success, as well as for the personal dislike they sometimes aroused. The brothers were psychologically equipped to work independently of others' help, and were able to furnish for themselves the inner drive that independent workers must generate if they are to achieve their self-appointed goals.

Although the printing ventures were moderately successful, Wilbur was soon forced to give up his part in them. His health, which was never robust and always depended on outdoor work and exercise, suffered from the confinements of a printer's life.

Taking advantage of the new craze for bicycling that swept the country in the eighteen nineties, the brothers in 1892 opened a small bicycle repair shop. Here again they were working independently, and they did so successfully. They soon expanded from selling and repairing bicycles to assembling and manufacturing bicycles which they sold under their own trade names. The "Van Cleve" and the "Wright Flyer" achieved a good although local reputation.[8] Their sales rarely exceeded one hundred bicycles a year; nevertheless, the business supported them and gave them sufficient funds for their pleasures. Under the heading of recreation they included for several years their hobby, the pursuit of flying. It was not until 1904 that they gave up their bicycle business.

Their bicycle shop served them well. Not only did it support them adequately, but it gave them valuable training in mechanics. One of their great advantages over other aeronauts came from the fact that they were able, themselves, to build what they designed. Chanute, Samuel Pierpont Langley, and Hiram S. Maxim, for instance, all were forced to hire other men to execute their plans. The Wright brothers were able to build while they were designing. This cut their costs to very modest sums, and in addition it enabled them to test their ideas while they were being born.

Although many later considered that Wilbur was the chief driving force, at this time he was less active than Orville, possibly because of his health. Orville, while occupied with Wilbur in their bicycle shop, was also an amateur bicycle racer, and was considered a good one.

[7] Daniel Guggenheim Medal for Achievements in Aeronautics, 1932; Mark Sullivan, *Our Times*, II, 570.

[8] Sullivan, *Our Times*, II, 571; Adams, *Flug*, 68.

When very young, the little boys had been fascinated by a toy, called a helicoptere, which their father had brought home to them one day in 1878. This toy had two "screws" rotating in opposite directions, and it actually flew around the room. While their interest in the toy was not unusual, they used this early experience many years later when they concluded a study of propellers by adding to their machine two screws, rotating in opposite directions.[9]

As they grew up, flying kites—that means of vicariously enjoying the universal urge to get off the ground—appealed to the young Wrights. They became experts at this game and belonged to a kite club. That Wilbur himself did not think it significant was shown by his later remark that most boys were good kiteflyers. Their interest in flying was desultory and was confined to kites and vague observations of soaring birds, accompanied by the usual desire that they, too, might accomplish this same easy flying through the sky.[10] Thus by 1896 these two young men of twenty-five and twenty-nine years were dividing their time between their bicycle business, their congenial home, and simple hobbies such as kiteflying.

They were diligent young men, conducting their narrow lives with seriousness and earnestness.

Wilbur's dormant interest in flying was aroused by newspaper accounts, in the early eighteen nineties, of the gliding experiments of Otto Lilienthal. He had been following the work of the famous German with increasing curiosity when one day in 1896 he was shocked to read that Lilienthal had been killed while gliding. This sudden ending to Lilienthal's important work gave the final impetus to Wilbur's curiosity,

[9] Wright brothers, "The Wright Brothers' Aeroplane," *Century Magazine,* Vol. LXXVI, No. 5 (September, 1908), 641.

[10] Griffith Brewer, "The Life and Work of Wilbur Wright," *The Aeronautical Journal* (London), Vol. XX, No. 79 (July–September, 1916), 115.

and he shortly took steps to satisfy his interest. Soon Orville, too, was reading about this new field.[11]

It is significant that Lilienthal particularly appealed to Wilbur Wright, for Lilienthal was the first and foremost experimenter who actually, at this time, *practiced* gliding. He built a glider and made not one glide, as had many others, but over two thousand glides. Although he was an engineer and physicist whose writings showed great scientific knowledge, his flying activities were not confined to the study. Applying the centuries' store of knowledge, he made a practical glider and continued to practice gliding. This was his attraction for the Wrights—he was practical; he applied knowledge to achieve tangible, practical results.

Following his death, the Wrights were eager to read more about Lilienthal, and, if there were any, about other aeronautical experimenters. Their father's library, and that of the city of Dayton, yielded only Professor J. Marey's books on the subject, and these were confined largely to bird flight. The brothers then wrote to Samuel Pierpont Langley, secretary of the Smithsonian Institution, who not only believed in the possibility of human flight but was spending much time on aeronautical experiments. It is worthy of note that the busy secretary of the Smithsonian took time to reply. He gave them advice on reading and recommendations which saved much fruitless search, and started them directly on the right course. Like others, the Wrights were greatly indebted to Langley for this early help.

For the next three years the brothers read some of the most important literature on the subject and became aware of the long history of effort and thought. Following Langley's suggestions they read the Smithsonian reprints of Mouillard's *Empire of the Air,* Lilienthal's *Experiments in Soaring*, Langley's own publications, *Story of Experiments in Mechanical*

[11] Wilbur Wright, "Some Aeronautical Experiments," *Journal* of the Western Society of Engineers, Vol. VI, No. 6 (December, 1901), 494.

Flight and *Experiments in Aerodynamics,* as well as the *Aeronautical Annuals* of 1895, 1896, and 1897.[12]

They read also the recently published book by Octave Chanute, the first compilation of all previous aeronautical effort, *Progress in Flying Machines.* After Lilienthal died, Chanute was the greatest exponent of gliding in this country, and was, as well, making important contributions to the literature of aeronautics. He combined, therefore, the theoretical and the practical approaches to the problem.

Before starting his great work in aeronautics, Chanute had had a long and noteworthy career as an engineer. Born in Paris in 1832, he had been brought to this country by his parents in 1838 and was educated here. Spending his life in the United States, Chanute nevertheless kept in close touch with European developments, helped by his command of the French language. He had the advantage, therefore, of close contact with Europe, combined with intimate knowledge of all parts of this country. For about thirty years—from approximately 1853 to 1883—Chanute specialized in railroad engineering, and was so successful that his accomplishments in this field alone would have satisfied other men who were less active and less broad in their intellectual interests. He was the chief engineer for the Chicago and Alton Railroad. He planned and superintended the first bridge across the Missouri River at Kansas City. And he specialized later in iron railroad bridges.[13]

Chanute had many other interests, and his long life and active career even before he devoted his energies to aeronautics make a full biographical study. Through these many activities he became acquainted with men who later shared his enthusiasm for aviation. Chanute's wood-preserving business, for example, was a bond with Samuel Cabot of Boston, who

[12] Wright, "The Wright Brothers' Aeroplane," *Century Magazine,* Vol. LXXVI, No. 5 (September, 1908), 642; Brewer, "The Life and Work of Wilbur Wright," *The Aeronautical Journal* (London), Vol. XX, No. 79 (July–September, 1916), 116.
[13] *Dictionary of American Biography,* IV.

made wood preservatives; the encouragement of aeronautical efforts by both men was a continuing bond between them until Cabot's death.

After Chanute began the serious study of aeronautics, he published his investigations into prior efforts in *The Railroad and Engineering Journal*. Eventually these articles resulted in his famous book published in 1894. By this time Chanute had made many models and then had gone on to construct full-sized gliders.

Chanute himself made a number of glides. His reason for testing his own gliders himself is illuminating of the man's character: When he realized that he had been advising other men to get up into the air and to practice gliding in a full-sized machine, it occurred to him that this advice, while it was undoubtedly sound, might also be dangerous. He decided that he must himself do what he had been recommending to others. And so, at the age of sixty-four, Chanute went to Dune Park, near Chicago, with his assistants, Augustus M. Herring and W. Avery, and in 1896–98 made about two thousand glides.[14]

The Wrights and the rest of the world were soon able to read Chanute's full reports about his experiments, for he always published whatever data he thought might be helpful to others. He built several types of gliders, but his adaptation of the Lilienthal type was the most important. Soon the Wrights, in turn, were to use and develop the Chanute double-deck glider.

In addition, Chanute applied the Pratt truss to flying machines. By this device, which was a system for resisting stresses, one more link was forged in the development of flying. As Wilbur said once, in a rarely explicit tribute to the work of others: "The Chanute machines marked a very great

[14] Octave Chanute, "Gliding Experiments," *Journal* of the Western Society of Engineers, Vol. II, No. 5 (October, 1897), 600; "Recent Progress in Aviation," Smithsonian Institution, 1910 *Annual Report,* 145.

advance in both respects [control and strength]. . . . The double deck machine . . . marked a very great structural advance, as it was the first in which the principles of the modern truss bridges were fully applied to flying-machine construction."[15]

Thus before their personal acquaintance began, Chanute had influenced the Wright brothers, as he had many other workers.

By the turn of the century, by 1899, the brothers were seriously interested in the problem of flight. They had read, studied, and thought about the subject. They had gone so far as to formulate some conclusions about methodology and had decided to follow the Lilienthal-Chanute method of actual practicing. In this way they were carrying out their natural bent for the practical and empirical as against the merely theoretical.

Langley had pointed out as early as 1891 that the next problem in heavier-than-air flight was the art of flying. This, the Wrights felt, could be solved only through more and more practice. Even in the eighteen nineties the Wrights did not agree with Langley's approach to the problem of flight, for Langley was trying to solve it by making models first, then experimenting with powered models, and finally progressing to a full-sized man-carrying machine.

The Wrights believed this method to be expensive and futile. Nor had they any sympathy with the experiments of men like Hiram S. Maxim, who built full-sized machines without any previous practice in the air. As Wilbur later said, "We were astonished to learn what an immense amount of time and money had been expended in futile attempts to solve the problem of flight."[16]

Being expert bicyclists, the Wrights knew that one could

[15] W. Wright, "Some Aeronautical Experiments," *Journal* of the Western Society of Engineers, Vol. VI, No. 6 (December, 1901), 493.

[16] Brewer, "The Life and Work of Wilbur Wright," *The Aeronautical Journal* (London), Vol. XX, No. 79 (July–September, 1916), 116.

not hope to ride a bicycle by reading a book on the methods of bicycling. Analogously, one could not fly a glider by reading books about the subject. Even Lilienthal, their spiritual ancestor, had spent in the air only a total of five hours in five years of work, Wilbur pointed out, with over two thousand glides to his credit. No one, Wilbur stated, could ride a bicycle through a crowded city street, after hundreds of trial rides lasting only ten seconds each, spread out over five years.

Changing the comparison to horseback riding, Wilbur remarked further:

> Now, there are two ways of learning how to ride a fractious horse; one is to get on him and learn by actual practice how each motion and trick may be best met; the other is to sit on a fence and watch the beast a while, and then retire to the house and at leisure figure out the best way of overcoming his jumps and kicks. The latter system is the safest; but the former, on the whole, turns out the larger proportion of good riders.[17]

What Wilbur was pleading for was later called "flying by the seat of one's pants," plus actual practice.

The Wrights knew now of the previous attempts at flight; they had read of Maxim's flight of a few hundred feet in 1894, of Clement Ader's attempts in 1897. But to these practical men such efforts were no more worthy of the word "flying" than an infant's first steps could be called climbing Pike's Peak. To "fly" meant to them flight at their will, under their control, for the length of time they had planned, and ending when they wished. For they knew that if a man could get on a bicycle, ride it for the time he had intended, and get off at the place he had designated in advance—then that man was a bicyclist.

To think of flying at all, in 1899, was indeed a sign of mental daring. To plan such controlled flying entailed enormous

[17] W. Wright, "Some Aeronautical Experiments," *Journal* of the Western Society of Engineers, Vol. VI, No. 6 (December, 1901), 490–91.

mental initiative and courage. Moreover, the Wrights did not underestimate the difficulties. Wilbur himself said:

When we studied the story of loss of life, financial disaster, and final failure which had accompanied all attempts to solve this problem of human flight, we understood more clearly than before the immensity and the difficulty of the problem which we had taken up.[18]

Then he added another sentence which indicates the self-assurance that self-educated men and solitary workers often achieve, and which was one of the Wrights' greatest assets in the next difficult years. As they studied these many previous failures, Wilbur continued, "and considered how and why they failed, we could not help thinking that many of their troubles might have been avoided and that others might have been overcome by the adoption of more adequate methods."

At this point the Wright brothers were ready to begin to work on the problem of flight. Practical always, their first step was to build a glider. Even the question of which place would be suitable for their practice had to be determined. Then they would see to it that they would practice gliding to a degree greater than had ever been thought possible. Their goal was not the reading and thinking of the previous years but actual experimenting. As Wilbur said, "We soon passed from the reading to the thinking, and finally to the working stage."[19]

As the first step in the working stage, Wilbur in May, 1900, sent to Octave Chanute the first letter of the many which were to follow.[20]

[18] Brewer, "The Life and Work of Wilbur Wright," *The Aeronautical Journal* (London), Vol. XX, No. 79 (July–September, 1916), 118.

[19] Wright, "The Wright Brothers' Aeroplane," *Century Magazine,* Vol. LXXVI, No. 5 (September, 1908), 494.

[20] Chanute to Paul Renard, November 22, 1908.

CHAPTER II

First "Active" Experiments–1900

THIS YEAR marked the beginning of the Wright brothers' active aeronautical work, for which the previous years of study and thought had been only preparation. Starting with casual curiosity, the brothers had been led to serious reading on the subject. Drawn on by their growing interest, they had observed and studied the flight of birds; they had experimented with double-deck glider models, somewhat like the ones used by Chanute, although measuring only fifteen square feet in area.

By the time Wilbur wrote his first letter to Chanute, in May, 1900, he had become possessed by the desire to fly and the belief that it was possible. This yearning had eaten deep into his heart and his mind, and had pushed him forward to the point of making detailed plans for a full-sized glider.

Preparing for their first experiments with this glider, the brothers turned to Chanute for encouragement and advice. This was the beginning of a relationship which was to have significant results for the development of aeronautics; the young men, just starting on their career, fortunately wrote to the man who was established in the opinion of the world as the foremost student of the history of aeronautics. Fortunately also, Chanute lived in Chicago for most of this period, which facilitated their occasional meetings. Their frequent letters, however, were their main contact, and through them Chanute soon became one of the Wrights' few intimate friends.

The high ambition, careful thought, and scientific approach indicated in Wilbur's first long letter impressed Chanute and aroused his ever keen interest and sympathy. If intelligent use of previous experience is the sign of genius, the brothers early demonstrated a high degree of this quality. For they had selected, from the many aspects of heavier-than-air theory, one problem on which they would concentrate—the problem of equilibrium. This was, Wilbur wrote, "the real stumbling block . . . this problem of equilibrium in reality constituted the problem of flight itself."[1]

They decided to use the biplane form, describing it as "a structure consisting of superposed surfaces rigidly trussed along their front and rear margins, somewhat after the general style of the Chanute 'double-decker,' but not trussed from front to rear."[2]

Chanute's experiments had been directed toward finding a means of achieving equilibruim automatically. But the brothers planned to use levers manipulated by the operator for the purpose of controlling the balance of the machine. These controls, and especially the method of warping the wings of the machine, constituted the most important claim in their later patent and formed the keystone of their lawsuits; they were already planned in 1900! Thus, as Wilbur said, "the entire structure . . . would be given a warp like that shown in our patent."[3] In other words, already by 1900 the Wrights had planned the most important single element of their final successful machine, the method of wing warping.

If their system worked well, they hoped at this early date to proceed to the building of a powered flying machine. Years later, speaking of this time, Wilbur said:

we reached the conclusion that the problem of constructing wings sufficiently strong to carry the weight of the machine itself, along with that of the motor and of the aviator, and also that of constructing sufficiently light motors *were sufficiently worked out to present no serious difficulties.*[4]

[1] Brewer, "The Life and Work of Wilbur Wright," *The Aeronautical Journal* (London), Vol. XX, No. 79 (July–September, 1916), 117.

[2] *Ibid.*, 118.

[3] *Ibid.*, 119.

Considering that the brothers had never been in the air even in a glider and that gliding was only in its infancy, these early hopes for ultimate success might seem typical of the boundless optimism and high enthusiasm possessed by all inventors. For, as the brothers knew, other men, of great scientific learning, had not yet succeeded in this same aim. Chanute had confined his efforts to gliding. Langley had spent years of work before even his powered models were successful.

Younger men, as yet unknown, in Europe and scattered throughout the United States, were as deeply involved with aeronautical problems as were the two young Daytonians. Like the brothers, these men also had other occupations, and their variety shows that the desire to fly struck, it would seem, at random. There was, for example, William W. Christmas, a physician in Virginia, who was conducting experiments on birds and their wings. George Francis Myers, who had an M.E. degree from Cornell University, had filed patent applications in 1897 for flying machines of the heavier-than-air type. Lyman Gilmore, Jr., was mining gold in the Sierra Nevadas, for the production of what he now claims was a powered airplane with a steel fuselage and closed cabin.

Such examples, which could be multiplied many times, must include also scientific young men like Albert Adams Merrill, who had described to Chanute in 1896 an interesting form of glider and who was a charter member of the Boston Aeronautical Society. And there was Albert Francis Zahm, one of the outstanding students, even at that time, of aeronautics. It was through his efforts that Chanute became willing to take an active part in the famous International Conference on Aerial Navigation (of which Zahm was general secretary), held in 1893 in Chicago.

All of these men, and many others, had been devoting their time and energies to the problems of flight; some of them are even now active in aviation affairs. Thus in 1900 the Wrights

4 *Ibid.,* 117. The italics are mine.

were members of an unformed society extending throughout the country, all of whom were challenged by this unfinished problem.

Wilbur's first hints that their ultimate aim was to be first in this race for successful flying showed the brothers' intention to work out their plans carefully and step by step. Their clear grasp of each problem as it arose was indeed one of the factors that tipped the scales in their favor.

But at this early date the brothers considered their interest in flying to be merely a hobby, a recreation, even though their plans were so far matured that their projected glider included most of the important parts of their later successful machine. Their business was bicycles, for on that depended their livelihood. Flying and gliding must therefore be confined to their leisure time and must not be permitted to encroach upon business hours.

To keep their business and their recreation in strictly separated compartments entailed a constant struggle. For four long years, until they finally gave up their bicycle business and started to make aviation a business, they continued to struggle against the temptation to spend all their time on aeronautics. They constantly lost the struggle, for flying would not stay out of their minds and tended, increasingly, to distract them from their bicycles.

Before undertaking any active experiments, then, Wilbur was aware as early as 1900 of the disastrous potentialities of this hobby. This awareness led to traits that were later given much publicity: the brothers' extreme carefulness in money matters and their equal care in avoiding flying accidents. Wilbur was actually frightened of this hobby, which had already become an obsession in 1900—frightened of the financial burden it might easily become to him as it had to so many others and keenly aware of the possibility that it might cause his death.

Something of this attitude Chanute understood well, and he appreciated the cautiousness clearly revealed in Wilbur's plans. Chanute was interested in the details and descriptions of the Wrights' projects and in their theories. Their desire to learn appealed to this generous man who always responded to requests for information from serious students. Chanute made available to all not only his own data but also his patents. Indeed, his only reason for taking out patents at all, he once wrote to Hiram S. Maxim, was to establish priority.

At this early stage Wilbur was as willing as Chanute to be open and frank about his plans. But his reason was not, as was Chanute's, the furtherance and dissemination of scientific knowledge. It was, rather, the belief Wilbur held that no money would be made by the inventor of even the first successful flying machine.[5] And since there was no money in view, there was no need to keep his ideas secret. It seemed to Wilbur at this time, moreover, that the problem was too big for one man to solve alone. Therefore, experimenters must be willing to give as well as to receive help. And always there was the fear that even a successful worker would fail to make money.

In later years Chanute felt that the brothers had changed; that they had become mercenary and grasping in their desire to reap a fortune from their patents. Whether men change, or whether they merely develop along characteristics formed early in life, is a moot question. In this specific example it may be that Chanute's generous heart emphasized the sincerity of Wilbur's first letter, for his interest and sympathy were aroused by Wilbur's appeal, and Chanute immediately replied most cordially. Indeed, he furnished the brothers with the information requested within four days, and wrote them with a warm interest that encouraged a continuation of the correspondence.

The summer was the height of the bicycle season, and the

[5] Chanute, "A History of the Wright Flying Experiments," *Scientific American* Supplement No. 1639 (June 1, 1907), 26262.

brothers were forced to concentrate on their customers. They looked forward to September, when the rush of business would begin to slacken and they would have time, once again, to spend on their other interest. This year they had finally decided to take a vacation, and they arranged to spend a few months of their slack season (from September to January) away from Dayton and bicycles, and with their glider.

They had chosen a spot on the North Carolina coast, advised by the United States Weather Bureau that they would be sure of finding strong and constant winds there. The postmaster at Kitty Hawk assured them that this locality was well provided with sand dunes. Preparations kept them in Dayton until October. Then they packed up the parts of their glider, took a tent along for themselves, and started on the long and arduous trip to Kitty Hawk. They traveled for almost a week, this first time, to reach their destination.[6]

In spite of its inaccessibility, they found that they had chosen an ideal spot for gliding experiments. They put up their tent on the bar between Albemarle Sound and the ocean. Except for a sand dune, rising to a height of 105 feet from the center of the bar, they saw nothing but gleaming white sand, and then the ocean stretching for thousands of miles. Nature completed her workshop for them by furnishing many kinds of birds: ospreys, hawks, eagles, and buzzards abounded. The brothers were thus able to make further studies of these, their models.

Although this first visit was short, its results proved fruitful and encouraging. They had intended to attach their glider to a rope and to fly it as a kite, but with a man on board. He was to operate the controls, that is, the flexing of the front horizontal rudder and the warping of the wings. But the winds were not sufficiently strong to sustain the glider with a man, and so they flew it without an operator, themselves stay-

[6] Brewer, "The Life and Work of Wilbur Wright," *The Aeronautical Journal* (London), Vol. XX, No. 79 (July–September, 1916), 72, 73.

ing on the ground and practicing manipulation of the controls from there. As they later described it:

Suitable winds not being plentiful, we found it necessary, in order to test the new balancing system, to fly the machine as a kite without a man on board, operating the levers through cords from the ground.[7]

Being totally inexperienced, they found that it was difficult to operate both systems of control simultaneously, but nevertheless their system "inspired confidence," according to their later understatement.[8]

Just before leaving Kitty Hawk, they decided they must try to glide. They spent an entire day on the big slope about three miles away from their camp. This was strenuous exercise, since their propelling force for this first glider was measured not in terms of horsepower, but in manpower. Two men, one on each side, pulled the glider forward until it rose into the air. It is small wonder that their day's work resulted in only a dozen glides, with a total of about two minutes actually spent in the air.

But the results atoned for their exertions, for theirs was the first glider in which the operator lay flat on the lower plane. Their practice in this change of position from the vertical to the horizontal was a most important contribution. It was not only an act of physical courage (for it had been thought that the horizontal position was more dangerous), but it was scientifically interesting, since it cut down the wind resistance five times. Other fields had long since used this principle— sailboat racing, for instance, and dog-team travelers in the north. As Wilbur said, by assuming the horizontal position "only one square foot instead of five would be exposed."[9]

[7] Wright, "The Wright Brothers' Aeroplane," *Century Magazine,* Vol. LXXVI, No. 5 (September, 1908), 644.

[8] *Ibid.*

[9] W. Wright, "Some Aeronautical Experiments," *Journal* of the Western Society of Engineers, Vol. VI, No. 6 (December, 1901), 495.

In addition, their system of controls marked an advance over the practice of previous gliders, who had steered by shifting the weight of their bodies. Their controls, the sheet anchor of their later claims, to use Maxim's description,[10] were first tried and proved in the fall of this year, 1900.

The brothers returned home to Dayton, delighted with their successful trip. They shared their joy with Chanute, giving him full details of their work, including their novel way of surface-grouping and their effective rudder.

Chanute immediately recognized the progress they had made in the art. This year's work, he stated publicly some months later, had placed the Wright brothers next in line of great gliding experimenters, carrying forward the work of Lilienthal, Pilcher, and Chanute—who modestly described himself as merely an emulator of the other two pioneers. The brothers, Chanute said, had been so courageous as to try the horizontal position, and had boldly made experiments not tried by their famous predecessors.[11]

Even before he made this speech Chanute had indicated his belief in the value of their work. When Chanute received Wilbur's report about their first season at Kitty Hawk, he asked for permission "to allude to your experiments in such brief and guarded way as you may indicate"[12] in a forthcoming article. It was indeed an achievement to have this request from the greatest authority in the country.

But the Wrights were never impressed by mere paper profits. Maintaining their own balance as well as they had their glider's, they received this compliment sagaciously and carefully. They gave Chanute explicit directions concerning what he might publish about their work, but they forbade all descriptions of their machine and their methods.

[10] Hiram S. Maxim, *Artificial and Natural Flight,* 167.

[11] W. Wright, "Some Aeronautical Experiments," *Journal* of the Western Society of Engineers, Vol. VI, No. 6 (December, 1901), 489.

[12] Octave Chanute, "Aerial Navigation," *Cassier's Magazine,* Vol. XX, No. 2 (June, 1901), 111–23.

In only five months they had changed greatly. In the previous June, Wilbur had emphasized his belief that one man alone could make only a small contribution to the problem and that therefore the greatest achievement would be to stimulate others. By this November, Wilbur had forgotten the value of being a missionary of aeronautical progress; the value of stimulating other men's work was fading out of sight. Without doubt, the excellent result obtained during their first season at Kitty Hawk had caused this rapid change, for, Wilbur said later, their method had proved more successful "than we had dared to expect."[13] Another reason for hesitating to allow Chanute to describe their results was that they felt they had not yet made complete and exhaustive tests.

With varying expressions of these basic reasons, the brothers maintained throughout their career this unwillingness to have their work described by others. They would themselves occasionally give full details of their work to certain individuals—and to Chanute they gave them gladly and unhesitatingly, particularly in this early period. But the data were for the use of the individuals alone. They consistently refused to make known to the world any published descriptions of their methods and the construction of their machine.

This first display of the Wrights' hesitancy ended by their giving to Chanute modified approval of his mention of their work. Soon the first published allusion to the Wright brothers was ready for *Cassier's Magazine*. The detail of what to call the brothers had first to be settled—always a difficulty when writing about these two men who worked in harmony and indeed with unanimity. Wilbur objected to the use of their initials only. Also, they did not wish to be described as manufacturers, unless the other experimenters were similarly mentioned. When Chanute then suggested "W. Wright & Bro." or "Wright Brothers," Wilbur denied that they had any prefer-

---

[13] W. Wright, "Some Aeronautical Experiments," *Journal* of the Western Society of Engineers, Vol. VI, No. 6 (December, 1901), 498.

ence at all but suggested the old-fashioned and dignified term, *"Messrs.* Wilbur and Orville Wright."[14] Like most of their personal preferences, this, too, was disregarded, for posterity has preferred to call them simply the Wright brothers.

The Wrights were eager to meet Chanute, who had already proved to be a helpful friend. Their scientific debt to Chanute's work was enormous, since their first glider was, so Wilbur said the following year, a Chanute double-decker, plus "a smaller surface placed a short distance in front of the main surfaces. ... In the main frame a few changes were also made *in the details of construction* and trussing employed by Mr. Chanute." But they believed that their own changes relieved them of any undue obligation to their predecessor, for three pages further on in this same address Wilbur stated that they had started this year's work "with almost revolutionary theories on many points, and an entirely untried form of machine."[15] By 1908 the brothers had again modified their description of the 1900 glider, and wrote of "the apparently rigid system of superposed surfaces, *invented* by Wenham, and *improved* by Stringfellow and Chanute."[16]

The brothers realized, at least in this period, the value of the Pratt truss to aeronautics. Their later hesitancy in acknowledging the importance of Chanute's gliders to their own work was brought out clearly in 1912 when Wilbur testified during a lawsuit as follows:

XQ. 105. So far as the construction of the main supporting surfaces of your glider was concerned (except that you did not truss

[14] Chanute, "Aerial Navigation," *Cassier's Magazine,* Vol. XX, No. 2 (June, 1901), 119.

[15] W. Wright, "Some Aeronautical Experiments," *Journal* of the Western Society of Engineers, Vol. VI, No. 6 (December, 1901), 495, 498. The italics are mine.

[16] Wright, "The Wright Brothers' Aeroplane," *Century Magazine,* Vol. LXXVI, No. 5 (September, 1908), 644. The italics are mine.

them diagonally from front to rear) you took the prior Chanute gliders as your model?

A. [Wilbur Wright testifying] We never built a glider trussed laterally exactly like Mr. Chanute's glider, which was a Pratt bridge truss, but we adopted a modification of this style of truss, as we considered it sound engineering design.

XQ. 105a. Then, with the explanation you have given, is your answer an affirmative?

A. The construction used by Mr. Chanute in his experiments undoubtedly influenced us in designing this portion of our own apparatus.[17]

Chanute's interest and encouragement, the brothers always believed, constituted his greatest contribution to their work and indeed to the art of flying. There is no doubt that this was a primary factor in their ultimate success, for Chanute's enthusiastic interest in their work never flagged, even when they themselves were most discouraged.[18]

By the end of 1900 there was already a cordial relationship between the older scientist and the younger men. Wilbur hoped that Chanute would visit them in Dayton, where they could show him a model of the large machine left at Kitty Hawk. There were many topics on which they were eager to have Chanute's opinion, including a new law which they had formulated relating to the angle of incidence. They believed that this law might have some importance.

This first year of "active experimentation," as they called it, ended on a note of enthusiastic hope. Describing the work done in 1900, Wilbur said:

Everything seemed to us to confirm the correctness of our original opinions, (1) that practice is the key to the secret of flying; (2) that it is practicable to assume the horizontal position; (3) that a smaller surface set at a negative angle in front of the main bearing

[17] U. S. Circuit Court, Western District of New York, I, 565 (Wilbur Wright on February 20, 1912).

[18] Fred C. Kelly, "How the Wright Brothers Began," *Harper's Magazine*, Vol. 179 (October, 1939), 479.

surfaces, or wings, will largely counteract the effect of the fore and aft travel of the center of pressure, (4) that steering up and down can be attained with a rudder, without moving the position of the operator's body, (5) that twisting the wings so as to present their ends to the wind at different angles is a more prompt and efficient way of maintaining lateral equilibrium than shifting the body of the operator.[19]

These five points sum up the large advances made by the end of this year. Small wonder that the brothers, having tasted success, were sanguine about the future. They had made a good start on the road to fame, with Chanute helping to put them there.

[19] W. Wright, "Some Aeronautical Experiments," *Journal* of the Western Society of Engineers, Vol. VI, No. 6 (December, 1901), 498.

CHAPTER III

"Reluctantly . . . into the Scientific Side"—1901

T HIS WAS A YEAR of struggle, disappointment, and mental crisis. But at the end of 1901 the brothers were more deeply involved than ever before with the problems of flying, even though they had again determined to continue with their bicycle business and even to expand it.

Their energy was boundless, for their bicycle business consumed from twelve to fourteen hours a day, from March through June. Although they never worked on Sundays, their program of six working days of twelve to fourteen hours each was a heavy one. Somehow they found time also to build a new glider and to plan further experiments for their next trip to Kitty Hawk. In addition, a short article entitled "Angle of Incidence," written by Wilbur, appeared in the July *Aeronautical Journal,* London.

In carrying out this amount of work, they were helped by the fact that they were working for and by themselves and could thus grasp any free moments during the day to let their thoughts wander to Kitty Hawk and their glider. The closeness of their lives was another, inestimable advantage: sharing the same business, interested in the same hobby, returning at night to the same home, they could at all times continue their discussions and plans without interruption. Each had the pleasure of another person's interest and sympathy; their harmony was so complete that they never needed to adjust to any other human being, for they functioned together as a unit. Thus it is obvious why they made so few intimate friends, for each stimulated the other's creative energies.

The exact contribution of each brother to their joint success is a futile inquiry, for their relationship functioned as a whole, not as two separate parts. Moreover, since there were two men working together harmoniously on the same problem, they had double the energy available to one worker. They could therefore carry through a heavy program, such as this year entailed, which would have been impossible to one man working alone.

The previous year's results had been so encouraging that the brothers did not wait until the fall of 1901 to return to Kitty Hawk. Instead, they arranged their bicycle business so as to leave Dayton soon after the peak of their busiest time, July 4, had passed. Their 1901 glider was to be exactly like the glider of 1900, but it had almost twice the surface area.

To try a glider with an area of 308 square feet was a mark of courage, for so large a machine had, Wilbur noted, "never before been deemed controllable. The Lilienthal machine had an area of 151 square feet; that of Pilcher 165 square feet [the area of the 1900 Wright glider]; and the Chanute double decker 134 square feet."[1]

Having learned the necessity for protecting their glider from the elements at Kitty Hawk, they first built a shed, making it sufficiently wide to house the machine when fully assembled. They hinged the doors so that they would form awnings at each end of the building, making what would now be called a hangar. Such ingenuity and attention to all aspects of their problems were significant of their abilities. And yet the brothers later resented being called expert mechanics, a title of respect which they assuredly deserved.

Their own comforts were given far less attention than their glider's needs; they camped out in the same building that housed their glider, with a minimum of physical com-

---

[1] W. Wright, "Some Aeronautical Experiments," *Journal* of the Western Society of Engineers, Vol. VI, No. 6 (December, 1901), 499.

forts. In addition to two cots, their furniture consisted of one table, one bench, and some folding chairs.

This simple setting was the scene of their first meeting with Chanute, who arrived soon after they had prepared their glider and living quarters. A fantastic story has sprung up about this meeting. The Wrights never denied its accuracy publicly, and so it has been handed down from one biographer to another. But Wilbur knew it to be a completely fanciful account. The story goes that an elderly man, of impressive dignity, "appeared" one day at Kitty Hawk, watched their many glides in silent amazement, and then said, "Do you young men know that you have come nearer to the art of flying than any other men who have ever lived?" The story ends: "And the Wright brothers at once transfered their play into serious work."[2]

Chanute was irritated when this story first appeared and described it to Wilbur (on May 2, 1907) "as sacrificing accuracy to picturesqueness. He [the author] did not send me a proof as agreed, or I would have cut out that paragraph which represents me as coming out of the bushes and making an absurd speech to you."

The meeting as it actually happened was sufficiently picturesque, as well as being historically important. Gleaming white sands, a hot southern sun, and two young men of thirty and thirty-four, lean, hard, and angular, working so hard on their experiments that they had no energies (or interest) for more than the essential amenities of life. Chanute, a citizen of the world, bearded and portly, kindly and wise. At sixty-nine years of age his interest and enthusiasm were so great that he gladly made this long, arduous journey: first, the trip from Chicago to Norfolk; then a boat at ten in the morning from Norfolk, arriving at Nag's Head at 7:30 P.M. From there he was faced with an eight-mile trip—and not by automobile—

2 Herbert N. Casson, "At Last We Can Fly," *Pearson's Magazine* (London), Vol. XXIV (July, 1907), 96.

31

to the Wrights' camp. On arriving, he found the Wrights and
their glider—and mosquitoes worse than any in the memory
of the oldest living inhabitant.

It was thus impossible for Chanute simply to "appear" at
this isolated spot on the North Carolina coast.

Actually, this meeting had been carefully prepared with a
good deal of correspondence. The pressing invitations from
the Wrights urging Chanute to visit them had suggested a
plan to Chanute, who was trying to find a way of helping the
brothers. E. C. Huffaker, former assistant to Langley, had
just finished building Chanute's third type of glider. Although
Chanute was aware of certain faults in this glider, nevertheless he wanted to try it out, now that it was ready. Accordingly, he suggested to the Wrights that they all pool their efforts,
phrasing his offer modestly, in the following words, written
June 29, 1901:

If you think you can extract instruction from its [the glider's]
failure, I beg to make this proposition.

1. I will send Mr. Huffaker and his machine to your testing
grounds at my expense, and pay his share of camp expenses.

2. He will assist you in your experiments, in exchange for your
assistance in testing his machine. The latter I expect to be brief.

3. If you think you will want more assistance, I will also offer
to Mr. Spratt (the young man in Pennsylvania who is anxious to
see experiments), to send him down at my expense to serve under
your orders.

His wide acquaintance with inventors having taught him
the need for caution, Chanute assured Wilbur that both Huffaker and Spratt were discreet. He mentioned that fact, he
added, because the Wrights had told him they had no patents.
Chanute was worldly wise and knew well the difficulties and
possible complications of unprotected work in this field in
which so many men were working to achieve the same end.

On several occasions after this first mention in July, 1901, Chanute urged the brothers to apply for a patent, but they did not file an application until 1903.

When considering Chanute's offer of the assistance of these two men, the Wrights showed themselves to be as careful and conscientious about Chanute's money as about their own expenditures. They hesitated to accept the services of Huffaker and Spratt unless Chanute was sure it was worth the expense. Or possibly Chanute wanted to see if Spratt was capable enough to be used at some later date in his (Chanute's) work?[3]

As to the question of discretion, they felt sure that men who were interested in aeronautics were not the kind to take other men's ideas—a point on which the brothers changed their minds radically in later years. They themselves had benefited largely from previous work, and therefore hoped that their work would be similarly beneficial. On the other hand, they trusted that experimenters would not steal their ideas, and they on their part would not think of appropriating plans not their own. But—with several additional qualifications—they knew that it was difficult to be associated with other workers without finding their ideas suggestive.

In brief, the Wrights showed their realization at this time of the difficulty of drawing a wall between men's thoughts so as to fence off one man's ideas from another's.

Thus elaborately prepared, there occurred in August the meeting between Chanute and the Wrights. They had a full camp. The value of Huffaker and Spratt was indicated by Wilbur's description of them: "We . . . were soon joined by Mr. E. C. Huffaker of Tennessee, an experienced aeronautical investigator in the employ of Mr. Chanute, by whom his services were kindly loaned, and by Dr. G. A. Spratt, of Pennsylvania, a young man who has made some valuable in-

---

[3] Seven years after this visit Spratt developed a new type of airplane wing. Forty-one years later (in 1945) his son, George Spratt of the Consolidated Vultee Aircraft Corporation, developed it further and it was given many tests.

vestigations." Daniel and William J. Tate of Kitty Hawk also gave their help on many occasions.[4]

They first flew their new glider as a kite, as they had done in 1900. But its action was not what they had expected. Again Chanute encouraged them, as they implied in a later account: "Mr. Chanute, who witnessed the experiments, told us that the trouble was not due to poor construction of the machine. He saw only one other explanation—that the tables of air-pressures in general use were incorrect."[5]

Then they tried gliding and covered over 300 feet. Again the glider did not control as they had expected. It was carried up into the position from which Lilienthal had had difficulty in extricating himself. Once again Chanute buoyed their spirits, as they themselves wrote: "Mr. Chanute assured us that, both in control and in weight per horse-power, the results obtained were better than those of any of our predecessors."[6]

Even after hearing these words of high praise, the brothers were dissatisfied. They reduced the depths of curvature of their surfaces, and made glides of 366 feet and 389 feet. But the glider continued to behave in a manner contrary to their expectations. They had based their work on the tables of air pressures on surfaces compiled by their predecessors, and were puzzled and dismayed when their own observations cast some doubt on the correctness of these tables. In short, they had failed in the one important problem—control—and in spite of Chanute's encouragement and approval of their experiments, they were disheartened and their enthusiasm began to ebb.

As is usual in such times of trial and tribulation, even the weather seemed to turn against them. It rained constantly for days. Then the wind blew steadily from the south—and they

[4] W. Wright, "Some Aeronautical Experiments," *Journal* of the Western Society of Engineers, Vol. VI, No. 6 (December, 1901), 499, 500.

[5] Wright, "The Wright Brothers' Aeroplane," *Century Magazine,* Vol. LXXVI, No. 5 (September, 1908), 645.

[6] *Ibid.,* 646.

OCTAVE CHANUTE

William Avery in a Chanute glider at
the St. Louis Exposition, 1904

Wilbur Wright in early glider, 1901

had relied on a northeast wind, which had prevailed the previous year. Convinced that this was the wrong season for work at Kitty Hawk and that this season had been a failure, they left their camp on August 22 and went home to Dayton. They were completely discouraged and doubted that they would ever again resume work. Arriving home, Wilbur made the rash prophecy that men would, no doubt, "some time fly, but that it would not be within our lifetime."[7]

The brothers felt that the firm ground on which they had relied had given way. Too many problems remained to be worked out in respect to the main one of balance and control. Too much time would be needed to make new tables and new sets of calculations. They would not be drawn into this uncharted sea. Even if they were to succeed where others had failed—in correcting the calculations—it was not likely that their work would ever pay them dividends. Flying would not be achieved in their lifetime.

At this point Chanute came to their help, attacking with great tact what seemed to be an impasse. He agreed with their view that aeronautics would not be financially profitable, writing to them on December 27, 1901: "The view which you take, that the time spent in aeronautical investigations is a dead financial loss, is eminently sagacious and wise." Writing about the brothers in January, 1902, to James Means of Boston (editor of the famous *Aeronautical Annuals* of 1895 through 1897), he described their attitude:

Mr. Wright . . . has made a very considerable advance upon my own practice, but he is too sensible to devote his whole time to it. He treats his experiments as a vacation sport . . . . He is a manufacturer of bicycles and hopes to make a fortune. He expects another vacation next fall.

Chanute had earlier been faced with the same problem. He, too, had had to devote himself to his business, giving to aero-

[7] Brewer, "The Life and Work of Wilbur Wright," *The Aeronautical Journal* (London), Vol. 20, No. 79 (July–September, 1916), 120.

nautics only his intermittent attention; only in recent years had he been able to spend time and money on this interest. He had begun to be actively interested in flying when still very young (before 1860), but his interest had so interfered with his business that he had had to take definite steps to control it, and he described his means of doing this with some amusement years later:

... in 1874 all the accumulated material was rolled up into a bundle and red tape tied around it, a resolution being taken that it should not be undone until the subject could be taken up again without detriment to any duty. It was fourteen years before the knot was untied.[8]

By 1901, forty years after his first interest began, Chanute had made sufficient money to be able to devote much time and some funds to aeronautics. As he wrote to Thomas Moy in England, explaining his position: "Singular as it may seem I do not care to increase my present fortune. I have divided it up among my children and wife, so as to leave each a modest competence, which I deem the happiest and safest."

This, then, was Chanute's long experience with the seductiveness of aeronautics when he received Wilbur's letters complaining of the same difficulty. It seemed wise, in view of his own experience, that the Wrights try to make their fortune in bicycles, and then resume their aeronautical experiments.

However Chanute thought their work so promising that he was reluctant to have them stop. He wanted to preserve the results they had so far attained, and induced Wilbur to address the Western Society of Engineers, of which Chanute was president. It is an index of Chanute's influence over the brothers at this period that Wilbur accepted the invitation, for making speeches was always to be a rare (and to them painful) occasion.

Wilbur's courage, an outstanding characteristic of both

[8] Chanute, "Experiments in Flying," *McClure's Magazine*, Vol. XV, No. 2 (June, 1900), 127.

54

brothers, was barely equal to the strain of delivering this lecture. Even the possibility of having a "Ladies Night" could not increase his already great terror—but he did not wish ladies to be admitted if that meant that he had to wear what was then called "full dress."[9] This maiden speech was unlike their later articles. From now on the published writings of the brothers were generally brief and rather dry articles in popular magazines. This paper gives evidence of much careful preparation, although Wilbur felt that he had insufficient time to prepare an elaborate talk; and he hoped that Chanute would not feature him prominently in the evening's program.

In his speech Wilbur described in great detail their 1900 and 1901 gliders and experiments, acknowledging the importance of the work of Lilienthal, Pilcher, and Chanute. He indicated clearly his belief that powered flying was already possible, as soon as men could learn to balance and to steer, "for all other difficulties are of minor importance."[10] Giving little indication of their own discouragement, the paper ended with eight points which had been demonstrated by their two years of active work.

By this speech, if they had done nothing more in this field, the Wrights would have become well known. Modest though it was, it challenged the accuracy of accepted formulae. It was also a challenge, issued by these younger disciples of the gliding school, to the Langley school which believed in experimenting with powered models. For, Wilbur said, the skill that was essential to successful powered flight would probably come through soaring—a step beyond gliding.[11]

The articles reached scientists in this country and abroad; Chanute himself addressed and sent out 150 reprints to such well-known men as James Means and Samuel Cabot of Bos-

[9] Kelly, *The Wright Brothers*, 73.

[10] W. Wright, "Some Aeronautical Experiments," *Journal* of the Western Society of Engineers, Vol. VI, No. 6 (December, 1901), 490.

[11] *Ibid.*, 508.

ton, and to Lawrence Hargrave in New South Wales. Another 150 reprints were bought and presented to the brothers by Chanute.

Wilbur's speech received enthusiastic comments from the men to whom Chanute sent it as well as from some members of the Society who had heard it delivered. When Chanute was correcting the proofs, he wrote to Wilbur on November 27, 1901: "It is a devilish good paper, which will be extensively quoted." His enthusiasm was justified, for the paper was reprinted in the Smithsonian Institution's annual report for 1902—a rare scientific honor, achieved by the Wrights only once again.

An immediate and most important result of this speech was its effect on the Wrights themselves. Working over the manuscript for publication after it had been presented to the Society, the brothers found that their interest was renewed in the problems which had so dismayed them a few months before. Wilbur's speech had included such strong statements about the inaccuracy of other sets of figures that the brothers began to feel they must verify their own observations before publishing this challenge to accepted authorities. A later biographer states that they deleted from the published record of the speech most of their criticisms of the available scientific data. They must, they felt, establish their conclusions without possibility of being challenged.[12]

In later years the Wrights were less hesitant about expressing these opinions, and wrote:

The experiments of 1901 were far from encouraging . . . we saw that the calculations upon which all flying-machines had been based were unreliable, and that all were simply groping in the dark. Having set out with absolute faith in the existing scientific data, we were driven to doubt one thing after another, till finally, after two years of experiment, we cast it all aside, and decided to

[12] Kelly, "How the Wright Brothers Began," *Harper's Magazine,* Vol. 179 (October, 1939), 479.

rely entirely upon our own investigations. Truth and error were everywhere so intimately mixed as to be undistinguishable.[13]

They used even stronger words in describing Langley's measurements, writing, "Yet a critical examination of the data upon which he [Langley] based his conclusions as to the pressures at small angles shows results so various as to make his conclusions little better than guess-work."

The brothers now found that they could not keep to their decision, made after returning from Kitty Hawk, to abandon their experiments. They said, "We could not keep our minds off of the puzzling things we had observed, nor keep from studying possible solutions of our difficulties." And also, "Before long we were as deeply interested as before."[14] Unwillingly they took up the scientific aspect of their problems, as they wrote later: "We had taken up aeronautics merely as a sport. We reluctantly entered upon the scientific side of it. But we soon found the work so fascinating that we were drawn into it deeper and deeper."[15]

It was due to Chanute's proddings and interest, as well, that they continued with their work. He not only kept their enthusiasm alive, since he believed in the importance of what they were doing, but he also wished, for the sake of science, to determine whether the accepted tables were accurate or whether they were indeed invalidated by the Wrights' results. He was concerned by their tentative conclusions about the inaccuracies of Lilienthal's coefficients.

The brothers built two testing machines. In the second, which was a small wind tunnel, they tested the actions of about two hundred wing models. These studies entailed the use of complicated mathematical formulae, in which com-

[13] Wright, "The Wright Brothers' Aeroplane," *Century Magazine,* Vol. LXXVI, No. 5 (September, 1908), 646.
[14] Brewer, "The Life and Work of Wilbur Wright," *The Aeronautical Journal* (London), Vol. XX, No. 79 (July–September, 1916), 120.
[15] Wright, "The Wright Brothers' Aeroplane," *Century Magazine,* Vol. LXXVI, No. 5 (September, 1908), 647

putations they were helped by Chanute. They compiled detailed tables, and several thousand readings were tabulated. Although, as their British friend Griffith Brewer said, "it is on these readings that the subsequent work of the Wright brothers has been based," nevertheless they have never been published. Nor was a description of even their wind tunnel available until N. H. Randers-Pehrson in 1935 published his excellent study called *Pioneer Wind Tunnels*.

Describing the importance of the tables for the Wrights, Brewer said in 1916:

These tables compiled by the Wright brothers have not yet been published, but they have been in constant use by the Wrights ever since. The tables of figures are contained in long pocket books, and members of this Society who have been with either of the brothers at any of their experimental flights will have observed them refer to these precious little volumes when making a calculation.[16]

In this same winter when the Wrights were starting their wind tunnel, the first complete wind-tunnel laboratory was devised and erected by Albert F. Zahm of the Catholic University of America. Scientific instruments for exact measurements were invented by Zahm, and important studies were made there and published by him. He also, this early, used his wind tunnels for the testing of other investigators' work.

The idea of using wind tunnels was an old one: it had first been proposed by F. H. Wenham of Great Britain, the originator in 1866 of the biplane and other superimposed multisurface constructions.[17] Wenham's wind tunnel was built and set up in 1871 at Greenwich, England—the first in the world. Thus the Wrights were followers of Wenham in both the use of biplanes and in making wind-tunnel experiments.

Later, in 1896, Hiram Maxim also devised and used a wind tunnel. A. A. Merrill, who was still in the early nineteen

[16] Brewer, "The Life and Work of Wilbur Wright," *The Aeronautical Journal* (London), Vol. XX, No. 79 (July–September, 1916), 120.
[17] Victor Lougheed, *Vehicles of the Air*, 149.

forties conducting tests in California in his wind-tunnel laboratory, as early as 1896 mentioned his plan for such a device to Chanute. Following these and other pioneers' examples, the Wrights, too, built their own wind tunnel. From the results they "formed a valuable collection of aerodynamic tables," Randers-Pehrson wrote, "which were later used by the Wrights as the basis for their design."[18] Their experiments and the tabulations of their tests continued into the winter of 1902.

At the same time that the brothers were beginning these experiments, the world's attention had been caught and its enthusiasm fired by a spectacular flight in France. It was a flight in an airship— but the public did not know or care to know the difference between an airship and a flying machine, for, after all, both flew through the air. Yet this popular excitement was undoubtedly a factor in the Wrights' discouragement, since they believed that experiments with balloons were of no help whatsoever in solving heavier-than-air problems.

This flight in October, 1901, was the first appearance of Senhor Don Alberto Santos-Dumont on their horizon. Five years later he was to offer a serious challenge to the Wrights, and the questions of his achievements versus theirs, and his methods against theirs, are still active issues. The later rivalry of the brothers and Santos-Dumont was heightened by the great contrast between their personalities. Santos-Dumont, apparently without effort, won the affection of the world; he appealed to its heart. The Wrights, at the height of their fame, aroused cold admiration.

In 1901, Santos-Dumont was known as a rich young Brazilian, who had been living and studying in Paris for the past ten years, and was now only twenty eight years old (two years younger than Orville and six years younger than Wilbur). His interest in flying had been aroused in 1888 when he

[18] N. H. Randers-Pehrson, *Pioneer Wind Tunnels*, 13.

was fifteen, by his first sight of a balloon, at São Paulo. His family (which, on his father's side, came originally from France) went to Paris on a visit early in 1891, and Alberto's interest in science, and his eagerness to study, were stimulated greatly. Another trip to Paris in 1892 increased his interest in ballooning.[19]

Possessed of great personal charm, generous, young, and rich, Santos-Dumont was also a serious student, benefiting from and stimulated by the great activity in France at this time. By 1897 he had made up his mind to devote himself to the study of balloons. Soon he was building and testing spherical balloons of his own design. At the end of four years of work, by 1901, he determined to win the prize of 125,000 francs offered by M. Henry Deutsch de la Meurthe through the Aero Club de France in the spring of 1900. After several attempts and picturesque failures, Santos-Dumont on October 19, 1901, flew his airship from St. Cloud to Paris, rounded the Eiffel Tower, and flew back to St. Cloud again.[20]

This feat won the Deutsch prize and aroused high enthusiasm throughout the world. Indeed, the effect of any flight by Santos-Dumont was always to create enthusiasm and hope for successful flying, as was attested by a speech made (in 1906) before the learned Aeronautical Society of Great Britain, which said:

Whenever M. Santos-Dumont begins to experiment there is a thrill of enthusiasm throughout the civilised world, and everywhere we hear the cry that the conquest of the air is at hand. Such a faith as this was, indeed, inspired when, in 1901, M. Santos-Dumont rounded the Eiffel Tower in his navigable balloon to win the Deutsch prize. When his navigable balloon experiments ceased, the public faith again grew dim.[21]

[19] Albert Santos-Dumont, *My Air-ships*, 30, 34, 38; A. Brigole, *Santos-Dumont: o Pioneiro do Ar*, 15, 27; Albert Francis Zahm, *Aerial Navigation*, 102 ff.

[20] Santos-Dumont, *My Air-ships*, 39–40, 202, 204; Zahm, *Aerial Navigation*, 103.

Having won the famous Deutsch prize after so many years of work and study, Santos-Dumont immediately gave it away. He called in the prefect of the Paris police and gave 60 per cent of the prize, or 75,000 francs, to the deserving poor of the city of Paris. The remainder he distributed among his own employees in gratitude for their help.[22]

Here is the keynote of Santos-Dumont's popular appeal, and the world did not hesitate later to compare this characteristic liberality of his with the absence of any similar action from the thrifty Wrights. Even after the brothers could afford a similar gesture, they found it impossible to do anything so personal and spectacular. This cannot be attributed to stinginess but rather to their completely different upbringing, background, and personalities. It was consistent with the Wrights' characters to avoid such an act, even though for them it would have been "good business." Santos-Dumont was also behaving with consistency, for he had given away another prize received the year before.

The final proof of Santos-Dumont's disinterestedness and the final comparison with the Wrights was the fact that Santos-Dumont never took out a patent on any of his devices. Even after his heavier-than-air machines achieved the same enormous success as his airships, he maintained this policy. His refusal to patent made all Santos-Dumont's improvements, devices, and inventions freely available to the world. And as he gave so generously to the world, so the world took him to its heart.

At the same time that Santos-Dumont was giving away 125,000 francs, the Wrights were seriously worried about business. Although Chanute had offered repeatedly to give them financial assistance, the brothers had refused. It was not that

[21] Eric Stuart Bruce, "The Aeroplane Experiments of M. Santos-Dumont," *The Aeronautical Journal* (London), Vol. XI (January, 1907), 19.

[22] Santos-Dumont, *My Air-ships*, 214; Eric Hodgins and F. Alexander Magoun, *Sky High*, 200; Zahm, *Aerial Navigation*, 110.

their experiments cost much money, actually, for they were able to keep their expenditures within their budget for recreation, and the cost of their machines was never large. Their problem was time: they were horrified to realize that they could not control the hours spent on their experiments. The time they thriftily allotted to thinking of aviation could not be regulated as easily as their financial budget. They were deeply worried by the fact that well over half of the past six months had been spent on aeronautics—and much of this time should have been devoted to their livelihood, the business of bicycles.

Now they decided to take their hobbyhorse firmly in hand. They would expand their bicycle shop. After struggling to build up this business since 1892, they had come to the stage of increasing its capacity. They must make it a success within the next five to ten years.

Their resolution was so strong that by December, the approach of their busy season, they stopped experimenting. Hiding their regret, they hoped vaguely to be able some time in the future to resume their hobby. So they assuaged their stern consciences—for the time being.

However much Chanute agreed with the wisdom of this decision, he was disturbed by it. Making an excellent prophecy he wrote on December 19, 1901: "I very much regret in the interest of Science that you have reached a stopping place, for further experimenting on your part promises important results, yet my judgment cannot but approve of your decision, for I see as yet no money return for the pursuit, save from possible exhibition."

Unlike many inventors, the Wrights did not believe that their ideas would yield a fortune if only they could obtain financial backing. They went to the other extreme in their fear that they would not ever receive a money return. Although Chanute agreed, with the exception of this prophetic mention of exhibition flying, he made still another suggestion to find a way of enabling them to continue their work. His idea was that some rich man might give them "$10,000 a year to go on, to connect his name with progress," and so he offered to introduce them to his acquaintance, Andrew Carnegie.

Chanute's kindness was much appreciated by the brothers at this time. His interest and constant enthusiasm heartened them immeasurably in this year of bewilderment and doubt. His latest offer was a temptation, for Wilbur had often desired a scientific career. This hidden wish for scientific training was an important factor in the Wrights' final success and in their personalities. Lacking a scientific background, they cleverly attacked the problems connected with flying from a practical point of view. But the knowledge of this lack was a personal sorrow; it made them feel insecure at certain times; and it was the basis for many of their resentments, the least of which was an objection to being hailed as mechanics, even expert mechanics.

Although Wilbur was tempted by Chanute's offer, he could not bring himself to accept it. The brothers' indecision about their future course was a great obstacle, and so the debate continued: Could they carry on their own business and their tests at the same time, and still do justice to both? Outside financial help would only increase this difficulty, unless they gave up bicycles entirely. They might consider the idea of entering a new line of business, but they did not wish to continue with bicycles and at the same time receive money for their work in aeronautics, which would have to remain a secondary activity. Such careful weighing of factors before they decided to refuse help is an index of the highest ethical conduct.

In the midst of their continuous debate, they found themselves making plans for the next season at Kitty Hawk. Unwittingly, they were continuing the same division of interest of which they complained so bitterly. But they would do it alone and independently of others' help—that clear decision they made and kept. The year of 1901 ended with this struggle. Could they continue their divided lives? Could their long work on flying ever be made to pay?

Other aeronauts were facing this same problem and would continue to do so, long after the Wrights had made their choice. Indeed, it is a problem that faces all creative workers— whether future results will ever justify work that is all engrossing and that may promise big results, but which may never, on the other hand, give a money return for even the time spent.

The acuteness of this problem for the Wrights was the primary cause that changed aeronautics from its nineteenth-century status of scientific inquiry into the twentieth-century business of flying. For the Wrights were businessmen, accustomed to a money return for their work. If they ever decided to give up bicycles, they would have to be sure before they did so that they had something to sell, something of money value. They would not give up an established business, with an assured although small income, for a new venture which as yet gave no indications of yielding any income whatsoever.

To these men of action the difficulty of making a decision was greater than any entailed in carrying it out. They would not yet acknowledge that flying was overshadowing their business activities, but, in truth, bicycles were already being edged out of their lives.

CHAPTER IV

Nearing the Goal–1902

I N THIS most important year of 1902, the brothers laid the foundations on which were based their prestige, their claims, their patent, and even their powered plane. The Wright plane of 1903 was their 1902 glider with a motor added to it.

They changed radically in this year of 1902: At its start they were coming out of the depression that followed their 1901 season at Kitty Hawk and the indecision that had perturbed them so deeply. Rebounding, they were almost optimistic. In January, Wilbur decided that a successful flying machine was likely to come within a few years—*if* the problem could be given careful and constant and thorough study. (Here was a change from his not-in-our-lifetime prediction made only a few months before!) By the end of the year the brothers were planning the last step toward their goal—the installation of a motor in their glider.

The year 1902 began with the usual bicycle rush, and the brothers were kept busy in their shop until June. Chanute helped them carry on their computations during this rush season, and long tables of figures were constantly crossing the continent between Dayton and California, where Chanute had gone for a few months' visit. Eagerly, plans were being laid for the coming season at Kitty Hawk, for then the brothers would test their tables and laboratory work in a new glider. In addition, Chanute was having a new type of glider built in California, and was planning to have two old gliders rebuilt. Thus they would have several machines, new and old, to test at Kitty Hawk.

The outside world was beginning to take note of these two men. Many letters of appreciation for the reprint of Wilbur's 1901 speech were being received in Dayton. These were from men to whom Chanute had sent copies, for Wilbur had given out only a few to personal friends. Many men, Chanute wrote them, recognizing his handwriting on the envelopes, had also written him enthusiastically about the Wrights' work. Captain Ferdinand Ferber of the French Army, who had been working on aeronautics since 1898, had this year begun to correspond with Chanute. Ferber, chief apostle of flying in France (so Chanute described him)[1] was later influential in trying to sell a Wright plane to the French government.

He wrote to Chanute this year that he was "in a State of *Admiration* [*sic*]" for the Wrights' performance. Lawrence Hargrave sent a card from New South Wales saying that Wilbur was clearly "One of the right sort." Sidney H. Hollands wrote Chanute from England requesting a photograph of the brothers; but they had not had their pictures taken for fifteen or twenty years and sent him photographs of their glider instead.

Many others, through Chanute's correspondence and Wilbur's 1901 speech, began to be interested in the brothers' work. Articles appeared in the early part of 1902 in *Feilden's Magazine,* London, *Illustrierte Aeronautische Mitteilungen,* Strassburg, and *The Automotor and Horseless Vehicle Journal,* London, all describing the Wrights' work and giving parts of Wilbur's speech. *Le Pays* of Paris gave a long description of the important experiments conducted in the United States by "Monsieur Wilbug Bright." An article in the *Scientific American,* New York, which reproduced parts of the lecture and the photographs, pleased Wilbur.

[1] Chanute, "Recent Progress in Aviation," Smithsonian Institution 1910 *Annual Report,* 155.

Aware of their increasing prestige, the brothers hesitated to publish their tables on tandentials and pressures. For months they discussed this question with Chanute. Chanute was the cautious one in this early period; several times he advised against giving too much of their work to the public, and always submitted to them his own writings when they concerned the brothers.

The brothers blew hot and then cold. At the beginning of the year they decided not to publish anything, as they might enter the proposed aeronautical competition announced for the St. Louis Fair of 1904. Chanute was on the committee and asked if they would try for the prizes of $200,000. In view of this competition, why should they publish tables that might help other entrants in this contest? If prizes were offered also for the best essay, they would surely publish their work. But since, unfortunately, aeronautical problems were sometimes complicated by financial considerations, they probably would not enter the contest unless they were likely to get back at least what it would cost them. As the brothers themselves realized, they never gambled; they always weighed possible gains against probable losses.

An article being written by Chanute for the *Pocket-Book of Aeronautics* (compiled by Major Hermann W. L. Moedebeck) raised the same question again about publishing their experiments. Chanute thought their results too valuable to be omitted entirely and wrote for permission to include the formulae for two of the most important curves. While Wilbur was pleased with the favorable tone of the article, he doubted whether they merited such a laudatory notice. As to publishing the formulae, the brothers could not come to a decision, for they were not yet sure of their work, although they had checked and rechecked with great care.

Fundamentally, they were afraid of being wrong. They lacked any appreciation of tentative results, which might have the value of guiding others to carry on their work. They believed always that work, like life itself, must be right or wrong, black or white. And so they desired to check their work in order that there could be no question of its rightness.

They had many other reasons for their hesitation, revealing their uncertainty. They desired to give their best results to the world, if they gave any at all. But the tables were too long to be included in full and might tend to discredit some of Lilienthal's tables. Whereas, if they published only a few tables and these seemed to agree with Lilienthal's, then other workers would fall into the same errors that they had. An additional complication was that it did not seem to them fair to permit Chanute to assume the responsibility for their tables by publishing them in his article.

The bewildering problem, as they felt it to be, of what to send for the Moedebeck book was temporarily settled by Chanute's suggestion that they make, at his expense, a sketch of the glider. But Chanute added to this suggestion the caution: "It is a question in my mind how much you should give away."

Wilbur promised to send some drawings as soon as he had time, and assured Chanute that their secrets would not be betrayed unless the sketches were accompanied by lengthy explanations. But the Wrights were not draftsmen and had (as Chanute pointed out to Moedebeck in July, 1902) "nothing but rough sketches, having developed their design as the work progressed."

The brothers never sent the promised sketches for this article. They reasoned that the article had lost nothing by this omission, since they believed that the 1901 glider had certain points of construction which it were better to avoid. They did not wish the errors copied, so they told themselves. Chanute, therefore, sent Moedebeck photographs of the glider. Thus, although the brothers did not ever publish their tables, nevertheless a good many men throughout the world had ample opportunity to study the Wrights' 1901 glider.

Orville Wright in Wright glider, Kitty Hawk, 1902

Official photograph, U. S. Army Air Corps

Wright brothers' 1903 flight, Kitty Hawk

SAMUEL PIERPONT LANGLEY

Chanute's wife died at the end of April, 1902, and at first he was so overwhelmed by his loss that he decided not to continue with his experiments. Upon his return to Chicago from California, his interest and enthusiasm partially revived. Slowly he took up again his plans for the coming season at Kitty Hawk.

Always on the lookout for promising aeronautical work, Chanute had met, while in California, C. H. Lamson, who had recently taken out a patent on a method for kites. Lamson was building a new type of glider for Chanute—a folding gliding machine to test Chanute's proposed rocking (or oscillating) surfaces. This new glider Chanute now proposed to send to Kitty Hawk, along with two old gliders, to test their qualities. The brothers welcomed this idea enthusiastically, for they would be able to compare the actions of these gliders with their own, giving a practical demonstration of the good and bad points of each. These tests would be of great help in planning their future machines.

The brothers agreed to rebuild the two old Chanute gliders after their busy season, at Chanute's expense. But one day after Chanute's return to Chicago in May, he was visited by his former assistant, Augustus M. Herring, who had also worked for Langley as well as assisting Chanute in 1896–97. Herring was urgently in need of a job and suggested that he do the rebuilding of the gliders instead of the Wrights. Chanute asked the brothers, who had not seemed eager to undertake this work, which they would prefer, since the gliders were meant to be a gift to them from Chanute.

Wilbur was glad to be relieved of this work. In truth, the brothers did not relish the job of building machines on which other men might lose their lives. Although this thought now seems tactless, considering that Chanute was an elderly man of seventy who was just recovering from his wife's death, the explanation may be found in the fact that the brothers were beginning to be increasingly aware of the danger of their game. Playing with the idea of mounting a motor on their plane, they began to take even greater care than before that no accidents should occur.

In addition, their time was much occupied at this period by their father's affairs and the complications in their church. Their bicycle rush was not yet over; they had much work to do still on their tables and plans, and in the midst of these preoccupations, Wilbur spent several weeks at Huntington, Indiana, on church matters. This dispersion of their energies, which they usually avoided successfully, was a great irritation to the brothers, and may have contributed to their inept response to Chanute's gracious offer.

Contributing to these influences in their lives at this time was a fear of what the world would think if Chanute sent his gliders to Kitty Hawk. Other people might get the impression, if the brothers' tests of Chanute's gliders failed to give good results, that the Wrights had made too little effort on Chanute's behalf. But with great patience Chanute wrote to Wilbur that he feared they would give his gliders too much, not too little, time and effort.

Although Wilbur felt that they had accomplished more work the previous year before Huffaker's arrival and when they were working alone, nevertheless they preferred that Chanute send an expert this year to test the gliders at Kitty Hawk. The next problem was to select the assistant.

Having visited the brothers in Dayton early in July, Chanute decided to go to Kitty Hawk himself, and suggested bringing Herring along. Prophetically, the brothers hesitated to welcome Herring, having heard that he was apt to claim a good deal of the credit for his share in previous experiments (notably those of Chanute and Langley). Finally, however, they decided that if Chanute were present at Kitty Hawk with Herring, there could be little danger of discord or future complications.

Chanute agreed with this opinion of Herring, for when

Sir Hiram Maxim was considering hiring Herring as an assistant for his renewed experiments, he first asked Chanute for his opinion. Chanute's reply of May 25, 1902, gave a careful description of Herring:

He has had much experience in experiments in Aerial Navigation, he possesses considerable ability, knowledge and mechanical instincts,—but, (how came you to judge him so accurately at first sight) he cannot easily be managed. I think that he can be useful to you provided that you make him follow your instructions strictly and establish clearly which are your ideas and which are his.

It was unfortunate that Chanute, with this clear vision of Herring, chose to bring him along to Kitty Hawk, although he undoubtedly agreed with Wilbur that there would be little danger if he were present during the visit. In later years this trip of Herring's to Kitty Hawk loomed large in the lawsuits brought by the Wright Company against Herring and his then associate, Glenn H. Curtiss. The question arose whether Herring had seen and copied the Wright wing-warping device after this visit, or whether he had himself proposed and used it on a model built in 1893 as well as on a powered plane built and allegedly flown in 1898, four years before this visit.[2] However, the lawsuit was in the future, and the difficulties with Herring did not begin until 1904.

Chanute became irritated with Herring soon after they left Kitty Hawk, and wrote to Langley in October:

I have lately gotten out of conceit with Mr. Herring and I fear that he is a bungler. He came to me in July, said that he was out of employment and urged that I let him rebuild gliding machines, "to beat Mr. Wright." I consented to building new wings for the multiple wing machine. . . . Doubtless he got some new and valuable ideas by seeing Mr. Wright's machine."

But then Chanute dismissed Herring from his mind, cer-

[2] U. S. Circuit Court of Appeals: Wright Co. *vs.* Herring-Curtiss Co. and Glenn H. Curtiss, VI, 29; Carl Dienstbach, "Herring's Work," *American Aeronaut and Aerostatist*, Vol. I, No. 7 (May, 1908), 155.

tain that he had avoided participation in the idea of "beating Mr. Wright," and sure that Herring was eager to make a fortune from flying. The brothers, on the other hand, were still in Chanute's mind primarily bicycle makers who regarded this aviation interest as a vacation sport.

They were too busy to worry about Herring's proposed visit and, indeed, were now less interested in Chanute's gliders than at the beginning of the year. They had been overwhelmed by his magnificent generosity in giving them the gliders, for Chanute had informed them of his intention. The offer of these machines, which would now be considered priceless exhibits in an aeronautical museum, was a touching gesture from an older scientist to two men of a younger generation. But by June the Wrights were convinced that the gliders would not be of great value in their work; certainly the possible benefits from comparative tests were not sufficient to warrant Chanute's expense in having them built.

The brothers were now focusing increasingly on their own work. They were distracted from it only by their father's affairs, which cropped up again in July and again postponed their visit to Kitty Hawk until August.

Having cleared up their father's problems, at least for the time being, and having made careful plans for meeting Chanute and Herring, the brothers started eagerly on August 25 for Kitty Hawk. This year the trip took four days, including a train from Norfolk to Elizabeth City, then a thirty-six-hour boat trip to Roanoke Island, a carriage from there to Manteo, and finally a sailboat to camp.

Arriving at their old camp they found that the building had been so buffeted by the elements that its ends had sunk two feet and the roof stood up like a camel's hump. After a heavy rain there were twenty inches of water on the floor. It took two days of hard work to raise the building and put foundation posts under the floor.

Their arrangements were more elaborate this year, for they had received permission through one of the Tates to erect additional buildings without paying rent for the land. Therefore they added to the main building a smaller one for the new glider.[3] They moved their own cots to the second story, leaving two extra cots and the main floor for visitors. They even took the time and energy to drive a sixteen-foot well. These construction activities took time, and over three weeks were consumed (until September 19) before the glider was assembled and finished.[4]

This glider of 1902 marked a great advance over the previous two gliders. The Wrights added a vertical tail at the rear, which was at first fixed and double. Soon they made it single and movable, or adjustable—this device had been patented by William S. Henson in 1842. A rudder was added to the front for balance. The wings were modified and their tips drawn on a line with the center; in previous gliders the wings were pulled down at the tips like a gull's. After a trial, they again lowered the tips in comparison with the center. The area of the glider was again increased: the two main wings had a surface of 305 square feet; the front rudder contained 15 square feet, and the vertical tail was reduced from $11\frac{2}{3}$ square feet to 6 square feet when it was made single. After a few experiments they attached the wires controlling the tail to the wires warping the wings—and the glider was finally in the form which they later patented.[5]

The brothers had finally evolved and applied to their glider

[3] Wilbur Wright, "Experiments and Observations in Soaring Flight," *Journal of the Western Society of Engineers,* Vol. VIII, No. 4 (August, 1903), 400.

[4] Brewer, "The Life and Work of Wilbur Wright," *The Aeronautical Journal* (London), Vol. XX, No. 79 (July–September, 1916), 75.

[5] Zahm, *Aerial Navigation,* 247; Octave Chanute, *Progress in Flying Machines,* 84; South Kensington Museum (London), *Handbook of the Collections Illustrating Aeronautics, 1929–1934,* parts 1–3; Brewer, "The Life and Work of Wilbur Wright," *The Aeronautical Journal* (London), Vol. XX, No. 79 (July–September, 1916), 122.

a three-fold mechanism for control. It was not Chanute's ideal, which was automatic control; this was operated by the flyer, by human intelligence.

They were now ready to test the new glider, and at first, as in previous years, they tried it out as a kite. Then they began to glide, with great caution, and avoided rising over five or six feet from the ground, and sometimes not over even a few inches. While they did not make many glides in September, after only about fifty they found that their glider was under almost complete control.

After a few days' experiments, these careful, cautious men were willing to believe that the machine was nearly perfect. They were jubilant. Their hard work at home on their tables was justified. Their method of control could be relied on to meet adequately any emergency. This was the first glimmering of real triumph. From now on, only practice was needed. As Wilbur said, "By long practice the management of a flying machine should become as instinctive as the balancing movements a man unconsciously employs with every step in walking."[6]

Soon after these first encouraging trials, at the beginning of October, Chanute and Herring arrived in Kitty Hawk. The weather was cold, and they wisely brought along warm clothing and heavy bedding. Two of Chanute's gliders had already been shipped ahead (he had decided not to rebuild the double-decker)—the older multiple-wing rebuilt by Herring, and the new one built in California by Lamson. The new glider was to test Chanute's third principle: "That of pivoting the surfaces to rock fore and aft on a stationary pivot."[7]

It may have been the lapse of years or the brothers' concentration on their own work that caused Wilbur, in a memorial to Chanute in 1911, to describe the tests of Chanute's gliders

[6] W. Wright, "Experiments and Observations in Soaring Flight," *Journal* of the Western Society of Engineers, Vol. VIII, No. 4 (August, 1903), 406.

[7] Octave Chanute, "Artificial Flight," in *Pocket-Book of Aeronautics*, 300.

in 1902 as being unsatisfactory, and to say of the oscillating winged machine that "It also failed to give positive results."[8]

Chanute, however, who was always modest about his own achievements, wrote to Moedebeck immediately after his return home: "My oscillating wing machine (built by Lamson) which carries out my third proposed method of obtaining stability, promises great steadiness. . . . I could test it only one day before coming back to my business here, but I have left it with Wright." And a few years later Chanute wrote about this same machine: "Built a full-sized machine, in 1902, with which good results have been obtained."[9]

In his court testimony in 1912, Wilbur gave an account of the sad neglect and final destruction of Chanute's gliders: "The machines were left lying in our camp until the building was blown down and everything in it destroyed a few years later."[10]

But these contradictory accounts, the loss of Chanute's priceless gliders, and the arguments with Herring, were all in the future. At the time Chanute returned from his visit to Kitty Hawk feeling great enthusiasm about the experiments there.

After Chanute and Herring left, the brothers achieved even better results than at the beginning of the season. In their last ten days at Kitty Hawk they made more glides than in all the previous weeks added together. In two days alone they made about 250 glides, the best of the year covering a distance of 622½ feet and lasting twenty-six seconds. They glided against strong winds, running as high as thirty-six miles per hour.

A great deal has been written about the physical courage of the Wright brothers, and the great degree in which they

8 Wilbur Wright on Octave Chanute, *Aeronautics* (New York), Vol. VIII, No. 1 (January, 1911), 4.

9 Chanute, "Artificial Flight," in *Pocket-Book of Aeronautics*, 300.

10 U. S. Circuit Court, Western District of New York, I, 616. (Wilbur Wright on February 26, 1912.)

possessed this quality cannot be overemphasized. In later years they themselves mentioned the risks they had taken in this summer, and Wilbur said in 1912 that they had taken the chances of personal injury in 1902 many times. During the 1902 season, however, they did not emphasize the danger, since their attention was focused on preventing and avoiding accidents. Even the following year, in a public speech, Wilbur minimized the danger and described one accident in which the machine was injured but Orville, the operator, "was unable to show a scratch or bruise anywhere, though his clothes were torn in one place." Continuing his account, Wilbur said:

"This little misadventure which occurred almost at the very beginning of our practice with the new machine was the only thing approaching an accident that happened during these experiments, and was the only occasion on which the machine suffered any injury. The latter was made as good as new by a few days' labor, and was not again broken in any of the many hundred glides which we subsequently made with it."[11]

No complete records were kept this season of all their glides, but the number was between seven hundred and one thousand. Their purpose was to obtain practice in gliding, and to continue scientific observations. The keynote of their success in avoiding accidents was that they refrained, then as later, from making merely spectacular flights. This intention, to which they adhered consistently through the years, was described by Wilbur himself:

"It was the aim to avoid unnecessary risk. While the high flights were more spectacular, the low ones were fully as valuable for training purposes. Skill comes by the constant repetition of familiar feats rather than by a few over-bold attempts at feats for which the performer is yet poorly prepared."[12]

[11] Wright, "Experiments and Observations in Soaring Flight," *Journal* of the Western Society of Engineers, Vol. VIII, No. 4 (August, 1903), 405.
[12] *Ibid.*, 406.

The brothers felt they had not even yet had sufficient practice and complained that with all these hundreds of glides to their credit they had had only, Wilbur said, about four hours "of steady practice, far too little to give anyone a complete mastery of the art of flying."

It was not with their machine but with themselves, they felt in 1902, that any faults might lie. As Wilbur stated it: "The soaring problem is apparently not so much one of better wings as of better operators." Their machine had justified the time and effort spent on computations and tables, as Wilbur remarked about this year's work: "With this improvement [in making the tail single and movable] *our serious troubles ended* and thereafter we devoted ourselves to the work of gaining skill by continued practice."[13]

Chanute was no less enthusiastic in his letters about this season's work. He wrote to Sidney H. Hollands in England:

> Their practice this year marks a great advance over any previous performance. The machine . . . could be guided up or down or sideways, with the greatest ease and certainty . . . the Wrights have now done much towards acquiring the art of the birds.

At this same time Chanute wrote to Moedebeck: "I am glad that this type (type 'Chanute' as Captain Ferber is good enough to call it) is likely to prove one of the types with which safety will be achieved. *As improved by Wright it is very steady.*" And to Baden Powell he said, "Wright is now doing nearly as well as the vulture."

As for the method of control, Chanute was pleased with it, although realizing that it had been proposed by other workers. He told Langley that he thought it better than Penaud's, but when Langley inquired further about the Wrights' doings and their control method, Chanute replied, giving no details: "I suppose that you understand that his method of control is not automatic, but requires the constant

[13] *Ibid.*, 407. The italics are mine.

action of the operator, being in that respect similar to that of Mouillard."

As in all methods, the question of priority of their wing-warping method was a complicated one. But the point of the 1902 season was that the Wrights' method had been tried and found successful. Zahm, in his authoritative book published in 1911, gives an exact description of their achievement, although he, too, realized the value of prior work in the same field:

Whatever improvements of efficiency and strength had been made [in the 1902 glider], these were of secondary importance compared with the provisions for projectile stability and manual control. *Here at last, after ten years' groping,* was an actual glider with sufficiently high centroid to minimize the pendulum effect, and with three rudders to give impactual torque about the three axes. These simple provisions had been previously pointed out in aeronautic writing, and, in the latter nineties, had been embodied in Mattullath's aeroplane, but not tested in the large machine, owing to his death.[14]

In later years the Wrights themselves were much more emphatic about this year's work than at the time, and in 1912 Wilbur said in his testimony:

This was the *first time in the history of the world* that lateral balance had been achieved by adjusting wing tips to respectively different angles of incidence on the right and left sides. *It was also the first time* that a vertical vane had been used in combination with wing tips, adjustable to respectively different angles of incidence, in balancing and steering an aeroplane.

... *We were the first* to functionally employ a movable vertical tail in a flying aeroplane. *We were the first* to employ wings adjustable to respectively different angles of incidence in a flying aeroplane. *We were the first* to use the two in combination in a flying aeroplane.[15]

[14] Zahm, *Aerial Navigation,* 247–48.

Even at the end of the 1902 season, however, the brothers knew that this glider was a great achievement. They had controlled it, and their satisfaction was increased by the knowledge that their tables and experiments had been proved right.

The Wrights left Kitty Hawk at the end of October in order to use their return tickets which expired on October 31. This time the trip took from daybreak on Tuesday until three o'clock Friday afternoon.

The season at Kitty Hawk had been so successful that they worked with great concentration after they returned home. Pressure was increased because their bicycle season began in January, and they had only a few months before it started; and their father's affairs once more were taking up much of their time. Early in November Orville began to work on a new machine for testing. They were starting also a new series of studies, approaching the problems from a different angle. Even though there might be some duplication of their previous work on tables, once more they were testing their results. They were so engrossed by their work that they had little time and no patience with academic discussions; they were interested in doing, in practical demonstrations, and in their own specific problems.

Chanute wrote them with great pleasure of the fact that A. A. Merrill was proposing again to try out his glider as well as a method for propelling the glider by a falling weight. But the Wrights shrugged off this news. They did not themselves agree with all of Merrill's reasoning, but since experience would settle everything there was no need to waste time on debate.

They were very scornful of the newspaper reports at this time of the many "successful" aeroplanes being built all over

<hr/>

[15] Brewer, "The Life and Work of Wilbur Wright," *The Aeronautical Journal* (London), Vol. XX, No. 79 (July–September, 1916), 121, 122. The italics are mine.

the country for the St. Louis Exposition. Engrossed with the problems of flying, they were amused at the reports that all these men seemed to have reached the final solution—except for small details such as what kind of engine to use! Thus by February, 1902, their interest in powered flight was growing.

Now the brothers began to show prejudices which were later to become strong and important motives. Most publicized, in its results, was their feeling against Langley and the Washington group, as they termed it, which had already been implied in Wilbur's 1901 speech and which, in spite of Langley's friendly overtures, grew stronger in 1902.

The basis of the difference was an intellectual one: Langley and many men in Washington were working on the problems of flying by experimenting with powered models. The Wrights were direct descendants of Lilienthal and the gliding school. They had received the impression in 1901 from Huffaker that the group in Washington did not sufficiently appreciate Lilienthal's work. On their side, the Wrights were increasingly enthusiastic about Lilienthal (in spite of the defects of some of his tables), and were correspondingly irritated by any apparent slight to his reputation. Furthermore, their early admiration for Langley had been modified by their decision, following their tests in 1901, that many of Langley's data were "little better than guess-work."[16] Underlying all differences of opinion was their uneasy awareness that Langley was truly a scientific investigator and that they themselves lacked such training.

Langley was told of the brothers' work by Chanute, who visited Washington soon after his return from Kitty Hawk, and was so much interested that he telegraphed them for permission to visit them there. He also wrote them a letter. Langley received a curt reply informing him that he would not have time to make the trip, for they were breaking camp. They

[16] Wright, "The Wright Brothers' Aeroplane," *Century Magazine,* Vol. LXXVI, No. 5 (September, 1908), 646.

stored as a grudge against Langley the fact that he had not mentioned his own experiments, being carried on on the Potomac.

Langley, because he had not yet received the Wrights' answer, wrote to Chanute for their address, and he sent them, through Chanute, an invitation to come to see him in Washington—at his expense. But the brothers had no time to go to Washington; the following year they refused Langley's tactful offer to lend them money for their experiments.

Realizing the value of Langley's interest, Chanute tried to increase it and to soften the brothers' attitude, but they never admitted to their confidence or friendship this scholarly scientist.

These intellectual differences and small misunderstandings made it inevitable that, sooner or later, the Wrights should decide that they, like Lilienthal, had been neglected by Washington and the Smithsonian Institution. In view of their intellectual irritation, it was not strange that Orville many years later took revenge on the Smithsonian by sending the repaired 1903 plane to an English museum.

In other relationships the brothers were beginning to show increasing self-dependence. Although well over fifty letters, and sometimes very long ones, were exchanged this year, the brothers nevertheless began to rely perceptibly less on Chanute's advice. Early in 1902, as in 1901, Chanute had again referred to the question of patents and had urged them to apply, saying:

I suggest that you take out a patent or caveat on those principles of your machines as are important, not that money is to be made by it, but to save unpleasant disputes as to priority.

At the end of this year Chanute once more mentioned this subject, saying, "I think you had better patent your improvements." Chanute was aware of the growing interest of other men in the Wrights' work, but his use of the word "improvements" was unfortunate, applied to a method which the brothers were beginning to believe was unique. This difference in point of view between the brothers and Chanute was not fully discussed by them until 1910, eight long years later, but even this early the Wrights resented the qualifications implied in this word.

At any rate, they had already drawn up patent specifications and were almost ready to file an application when Chanute wrote them this letter. In view of Chanute's long experience with the United States Patent Office, it is strange that the Wrights had not before mentioned this to him. They could have used his advice, for the Patent Office was, and still is, a difficult hurdle for inventors; it took from March, 1903, to May, 1906, before the Wrights were granted their first (and basic) American patent. But in 1902 they were, fortunately, unaware of this future delay, and this patent was merely one of their many plans—it was not yet a goal in itself.

In a purely intellectual form the Wrights had already begun to reap a small harvest from their three years' experiments. But they were too busy with their studies, their bicycle business, and once more with their father's church affairs, as well as with their plans for 1903, to spend their time in merely gathering laurels. They were, in fact, preparing for the final step of adding a motor to their glider.

Chanute did not know their intention, and in October he wrote to Langley, "They . . . have not intended to apply a motor, but they have acquired so much of the art of birds that I think they should proceed further." Chanute was, therefore, aware that a motor was the next step and indicated this several times. At this same time he wrote to Sidney H. Hollands in England:

I am very pleased that the course which I have been advocating for some years, i.e., to first work out stability and safety by gliding experiments before applying a motor, seems likely to lead to important results. *The Wrights are now very near to the point where it will be safe to introduce the motor.*[17]

And, again, to Moedebeck in Germany: "As soon as practice has been obtained to learn all the tricks of the wind, I believe that soaring flight will be performed, under favorable conditions, and that the time has nearly come to introduce a motor." Chanute wrote in a similar vein to Samuel Cabot in Boston and to Major B. Baden-Powell, president of the Aeronautical Society of Great Britain, and to others. These letters, written at the time, showed the eager expectancy which Chanute was working up in many countries for the Wrights' future work, laying a foundation of interest and good will which could have been very helpful to them.

In later years it seemed obvious that this next step of installing a motor must follow, and A. F. Zahm wrote in 1911 a breezy summary, saying, "the knack of balancing was finally acquired, and thus the glider was ready to receive the propelling mechanism."[18] Zahm gave Chanute's double-decker type a primary place in the development which, in 1902, seemed about to be fulfilled by a powered machine, writing of this type:

All who could appreciate it understood that the addition of a light motor would transform it to a dynamic flyer, navigable at least in mild weather.[19]

The fact was, however, that in 1902 no one had as yet effected this transformation, although many were trying to do so.

The Wrights were making elaborate plans for 1903: they would build a much larger machine, doubling the weight of the 1902 glider. The various problems of starting, controlling, and handling this large and heavy glider would be worked

[17] The italics are mine.
[18] Zahm, *Aerial Navigation*, 248.
[19] A. F. Zahm, "Octave Chanute," *Scientific American*, Vol. 104, No. 19 (May 13, 1911), 463.

on next. If all went well, then, they hoped, they could add a motor.[20] This high ambition led to specific daydreams: this year's work and next year's hopes might bring to life the possibility of making money out of this venture.

Chanute was aware of this coming change. In a letter to Langley in October, 1902, he gave a description of the brothers at this point of their career, which assumes importance because of his intimate knowledge of them:

They are Bicycle Manufacturers and repairers who find their business so slack at this time of the year that they indulge themselves in a vacation which is fruitful in results.

They have *heretofore* considered their experiments as a sport, likely to bring no money return.. . . . *They are very ingenious mechanics and men of high character and integrity.*[21]

[20] Orville Wright, "How We Made the First Flight," *Flying,* (New York), Vol. II, No. 11 (December, 1913), 10.

[21] The italics are mine.

CHAPTER V

Succès d'Estime–1903

IN THE SPRING of 1903, Chanute returned from a five-months' trip to Europe which had immediately spectacular as well as far-reaching results. He visited Germany, Austria, France, Italy, and England with the purpose of arousing interest in the aeronautical competition scheduled for the 1904 St. Louis Fair. Wilbur later called this a "missionary trip," and the results justified this term.

In France, especially, Chanute aroused interest in heavier-than-air flight, and so stimulated the French that for many years to come France was the nation most advanced in aeronautical activity. The Aero Club de France had previously concentrated on lighter-than-air problems; after Chanute's talk in April, it became converted to the possibilities of heavier-than-air flight. A French writer said, "This meeting can be considered the starting point, even more, the clarion call which sounded the reveille in France of the dawn of aviation."[1]

Chanute's speech of April 2, 1903, in Paris, was indeed one of the rare occasions which can be described accurately as the starting point of a movement. In this instance its first direct result was to inspire a large number of men with interest. There was, for example, Ernest Archdeacon, rich sportsman interested previously in subsidizing the development of bicycles, motor boats, automobiles, and balloons.[2] Immediately following Chanute's lecture Archdeacon founded a 3,000-franc prize for the first person to fly twenty-five meters. Captain Ferber, who had been working almost alone in France on

[1] Peyrey, *Les Oiseaux Artificiels*, 117.
[2] Adams, *Flug*, 95–96.

heavier-than-air flight until this speech, was encouraged by it to continue his experiments. Léon Levavasseur, the engineer, was also present at Chanute's speech and soon found a backer —M. Robert Gastambide—for his proposed engine and aeroplane. Thus was started the world-famous Antoinette (named, in truly graceful French fashion, after Gastambide's daughter). These were only a few of the men who started eagerly to work after April 2, 1903.[3]

A second result of Chanute's speech was that it aroused interest in Europe in the Wright brothers, their name having already become known through Chanute in aeronautical circles here. In his account of aeronautical progress in the United States, Chanute mentioned the Wright gliders as well as his own work. The French showed such interest in the gliders that Chanute promised to send back to France, on returning home, drawings of his and the Wright gliders. He kept his promise. Some sketches were published in the March, 1904, issue of *L'Aérophile,* the same magazine which had published Chanute's August, 1903, speech and other sketches.

These drawings and Chanute's speech circulated widely over the Continent, England, and the United States. From the Wrights' point of view they were unfortunately indiscreet. The brothers soon became less willing to confide in Chanute and bore him a grudge for this mention of their work. Actually, nine years later this trip of Chanute's in 1903 became a real stumbling block in their lawsuits in Germany and France! The wing-warping method was not disclosed by Chanute's sketches; but he had in his speech referred to it vaguely in a brief sentence. In 1912 the German Patent Office took, as the brothers said, "the extreme position that these few words were sufficient to teach anyone how to build and operate a flying machine in 1903, and that they canceled the right of the in-

[3] Adams, *Flug,* 100; Ferdinand Ferber, *L'Aviation: Ses Débuts—Son Développement,* 135.

[4] Wright brothers, Letter to the Editor, *Scientific American,* Vol. 106 (March 30, 1912), 287.

ventors [the Wright brothers] to any property in their invention in Germany."[4]

Although the Wrights did not believe that Chanute had given the details of their construction, they did believe that all aeronautical progress in France started in 1902–1903 following the news of their successes. Wilbur later wrote a definite charge that Archdeacon's first glider was "a copy of the Wright 1902 glider," and that the Voisin, Farman, and earlier Bleriot machines "grew from" this copy.[5] He stated, also in 1910, the brothers' opinion about the priority of their work in even more definite terms:

But when, in 1902, news of the superior results being attained by the Wrights in America began to spread among sportsmen in Europe, several Frenchmen began using machines which were copied from pictures and descriptions of the early Wright machines and which were called by them at that time "Machines of the Wright type." This was the beginning of modern activity in Europe.[6]

The issue lay in a difference of emphasis: some acknowledged that the Archdeacon glider, for instance, was based on the Wright glider, but only because that was the latest development in the long history of aeronautical thought by which the brothers, too, had benefited. As Alexander Graham Bell (interested in flying problems since the eighteen nineties) said, the Wright glider was an "improved apparatus of the Hargrave type as modified by Chanute."[7] Furthermore, as the Wrights themselves realized, pictures of their 1901 glider had already appeared in various journals, based on Wilbur's 1901 lecture before the Western Society of Engineers.[8]

[5] "The Earliest Wright Flights—A Letter from Wilbur Wright," *Scientific American*, Vol. 103 (July 16, 1910), 47.

[6] U. S. Circuit Court of Appeals, 2nd Circuit, Wright Co. *vs.* Louis Paulhan, Wright affidavit February 5, 1910, 264–65.

[7] Alexander Graham Bell, "Aerial Locomotion," Washington Academy of Sciences, *Proceedings*, Vol. VII (March 4, 1907), 413.

[8] W. Wright, "The Earliest Wright Flights," *Scientific American*, Vol. 103 (July 16, 1910), 47.

Another group believed that the later successes of Farman, Delagrange, Voisin, Bleriot, and Esnault-Pelterie had nothing to do with the Wrights' design. This group maintained that these men achieved success only after they broke away from the Wright form and reverted to the construction first suggested by Penaud.[9]

This issue did not arise for several years, but Chanute's speech was inevitably linked with the lawsuits brought by the Wright brothers and their companies against other airplane manufacturers in various countries.

In the meantime, Chanute's speech began to have immediate repercussions in 1903 in Dayton. Captain Ferber offered to buy the Wrights' 1902 glider, but they needed it for practice in their coming season and offered to build him a new one the following year.

Ferber tried out his own motored plane in June, 1903, but not in a free flight. Since it showed little success, he then suggested coming to the United States to visit the Wrights. They made it clear, through Chanute, that they would not welcome his presence during their experiments, softening this refusal by explaining that they would have been glad to see Ferber, *if* they could have four months in their season instead of two, *if* they had planned only to do further gliding experiments, and *if* they had proper facilities in which to entertain the Captain.

Another result of his speech was Chanute's reckless promise to send to the magazine *L'Aérophile* photographs of the Wrights. This was too great a demand on the shy brothers. They constantly postponed the ordeal of posing for their portraits; finally they screwed up their courage to face the camera; and then Orville got a piece of dirt in his eye which effectively prevented their carrying out this distasteful obligation.

Chanute reproved their cowardice, writing humorously on May 15:

[9] *Almanach des Aviateurs pour 1909,* 16; *American Aeronaut and Aerostatist,* Vol. 1, No. 8 (June, 1908), 223–24.

I am ashamed that men whom I have praised so highly in Europe should have so little courage to face a camera. Go and do so right away.

But the Wrights did not "do so," and three months later Chanute sent on another request from *L'Aérophile* for photographs and biographical notes, writing, "I know both of you to be so modest that I believe that this request will be most unwelcome." It was unwelcome, particularly because the brothers realized that there was not enough material for such a long write-up as the magazine planned. Chanute accepted their refusal, and wrote in August:

I will advise the "Aerophile" that you decline to be written up at present, but I hope that you will accomplish such success that you will no longer be able to resist the pressure for portraits and biographical notices.

The brothers continued to resist the pressure throughout their lives, and with unfortunate results: misinterpretation of their personalities and of their motives has been easier than in the case of other well-known men whose lives are an open book. Indeed it seemed that the Wrights' modesty was so great that it forced them not only to close the book of their lives, but to hide it.

The brothers spent almost the whole winter and spring of 1903 in intensive preparations for their coming practice at Kitty Hawk. The ambitious project of making a powered glider entailed more work than they had realized.

The first problem was to obtain the engine for their machine. They wrote to various automobile and engine companies throughout the country, asking whether they could furnish an engine for their purpose, which they stated clearly. Generally, the companies replied that they were too busy with their regular business; the other answers were also unsatisfactory. Chanute sent them details of Santos-Dumont's engines, but finally the brothers decided to build their own motor so as to be able to depend absolutely on its weight and power. About six weeks from the time they started their design, their motor was ready for testing.[10] Wilbur later said that Orville had designed the engine, and he described it as follows: "My brother prepared the plans of this motor, which was merely an automobile motor simplified and reduced in weight."[11]

The next problem was to construct propellers. Chanute's famous book, published in 1894, contained as many as forty-four different page-references to "aerial screws," starting of course with Leonardo da Vinci. Chanute included Dieuaide's variable pitch propellers of 1877, and quoted Maxim on the slip stream of propellers. But he ended his discussion of the subject by saying that little was known about aerial screws at that time.[12]

The Wrights described their first confusion when attacking this question of "the exact action of the screw-propeller, [which] after a century of use [by marine engineers] was still very obscure." They wrote an excellent description of the problem:

> What at first seemed a simple problem became more complex the longer we studied it. With the machine moving forward, the air flying backward, the propellers turning sidewise, and nothing standing still, it seemed impossible to find a starting-point from which to trace the various simultaneous reactions.[13]

They engaged each other in long arguments on the subject, and, they wrote, "we often found ourselves in the ludicrous position of each having been converted to the other's side, with no more agreement than when the discussion began."[14] By

[10] Orville Wright, "How We Made the First Flight," *Flying*, Vol. II, No. 11 (December, 1913), 10.

[11] U. S. Circuit Court, Western District of New York, I, 582. (Wilbur Wright on February 21, 1912.)

[12] Chanute, *Progress in Flying Machines*, 59, 72, 232, 238.

[13] Wright, "The Wright Brothers' Aeroplane," *Century Magazine*, Vol. LXXVI, No. 5 (September, 1908), 648.

June, they found a way of calculating the action of a propeller, but, practical always, they would not rely on its accuracy until they had tried it out.

Their third change in the 1902 glider was to add skids, which were designed as sled runners extending out in front of the machine. This device, they planned, would prevent the machine from rolling over forward on landing.

These three changes—the motor, two propellers rotating in opposite directions,[15] and the sled runners—were the only alterations made in the 1902 glider. The general construction of the machine was the same as in the previous year. Since they had made all this in their own workshop and with their own hands, it is no wonder that this winter and spring were busy.

They were buoyed up by their hopes for the coming season at Kitty Hawk and by their belief, even before they tested the machine, that they had solved the problem of human flight. Wilbur used those words in describing this year's work:

We now [winter and spring of 1902–1903] felt that the problem of human flight was solved and accordingly proceeded to make application for patent and began to draw up designs for a practical motor-driven aeroplane.[16]

Soon after returning home in the spring, Chanute visited the brothers in Dayton and saw that their motored glider was almost completely planned. During this visit Chanute told them of Langley's offer of financial help for their work, a fine gesture which did not, evidently, affect the brothers' antagonism to Langley's methods. Returning from Dayton, Chanute on June 7 reported to Langley the result of his visit:

It was only yesterday that I had the opportunity of seeing the Messrs. Wright, and mentioning your hint. They say that for the present they would prefer to accept no financial aid from any one.

14 *Ibid.*
15 S. Paul Johnston, *Horizons Unlimited,* 231.
16 U. S. Circuit Court, Western District of New York, I, 491.

73

The brothers were fully occupied. In addition to their new machine, they were busy with other aspects of aeronautics as well. They received from Chanute pamphlets in French and German, and while Orville was now able to make a good effort at reading French, neither of them could yet read German.

Their time was taken up also by the preparation of Wilbur's second (and last) paper for the Western Society of Engineers. Presented in June, this paper, describing in detail their 1902 glides, did not mention their current interest in motored flight. Twice during the discussion following it, Wilbur stated that they had not made any experiments whatsoever with powered machines. But he mentioned several times their laboratory studies and their careful collecting of data "for the study of the scientific problems involved in flight."[17]

This paper, like the previous one, was well received, and was published in the very next issue of the *Journal* of the Society, "thus giving it precedence," Chanute wrote to Wilbur, "over anterior papers." Chanute again sent out 150 reprints, almost all to the European aeronauts who had been so much interested by his accounts of the work in the United States. The Wrights, as before, sent out only a few reprints. But this time their list included Langley and Zahm. Like the previous article, the 1903 paper contained many pictures of their glider —and thus the 1902 Wright glider was seen by many men in many countries.

Chanute took great pleasure in their progress. It seemed as though the slight stiffness of the previous year had worn off and their differences had been forgotten, when another argument was started. Chanute was preparing an article for the *Revue Generale des Sciences*. "Should the warping of the wings be mentioned?" he wrote Wilbur, adding, "Somebody may be hurt if it is not."

The Wrights felt that the opposite was true: that the use

[17] W. Wright, "Experiments and Observations in Soaring Flight," *Journal* of the Western Society of Engineers, Vol. III, No. 4 (August, 1903), 409.

of their device, unless described in minute detail, might be harmful to novices. Nothing, therefore, should be published about it, and beginners should attack one problem at a time.

For a month Wilbur continued to criticize the article, and although Chanute made changes in the manuscript, Wilbur was still not satisfied with it. Finally Chanute sent a special-delivery letter saying that in spite of the many pages of description Wilbur had written, he had not yet answered Chanute's questions, "How is the vertical tail operated? Or rather how do you want me to say it is operated?"

Forced to face the issue squarely, the Wrights realized that they actually preferred to have Chanute publish nothing at all about their method. In fact, there were only three possibilities: to tell all, to tell meaningless generalities, or to say nothing. They preferred the last course, always.

They found a good reason for following their natural inclination toward secrecy: there was a provision in the French and German patent laws refusing a patent application if any of the claims had been published previously. Thus they wished to wait until the patent question was settled; for the Wrights had already filed applications for patents in the United States, Germany, France, and Great Britain, in March and April of this year.

Chanute tried to excuse Wilbur's brusqueness in the following pleasant reply, but he only made matters worse:

I was puzzled by the way you put things in your former letters. You were sarcastic and I did not catch the idea that you feared that the description might forestall a patent. Now that I know it, I take pleasure in suppressing the passage altogether. I believe however that it would have proved quite harmless as the construction is ancient and well known. . . .

I suppose that you did not know that that I had already mailed the article, and that time was an object.

This struck fire. Wilbur's tart reaction was that Chanute

75

misunderstood them: they did *not* use the "ancient construction" which was well known. Here was the argument, which continues to the present day, between the men who might have been considered to know most about it: Whether, as Chanute with his vast historical knowledge, believed, the Wrights' method was an application of an old device; or whether, as the Wrights believed, it was a new contribution to the art.

The discussion was not pursued at this time, but Chanute's feelings had been hurt. Although his interest continued, his care in avoiding intrusion on the Wrights was even more marked than before. He assured Wilbur that "nobody knows from me what you propose to do this year." Again, he reassured the brothers by telling them that he had written to A. A. Merrill in Boston that he had no cross section of their surfaces as he had not taken any measurements of their machine. At this same time he wrote to Merrill what might be called an apologia for the Wrights' secrecy (already beginning to be apparent to other aeronauts), saying:

Answering your question, I have always found Mr. Wright very frank and communicative; but with his success there has come a natural desire to work out himself the results of his investigations before making them public. I recognize this as rational, and I have forborn asking questions which would probably be answered. He did intend to publish his data on various surfaces, but (like Langley) he has postponed it for the present.

It irked Chanute that Langley had not recently published his data. Evidently Chanute did not allow for the fact that Langley was obligated by his agreement with the United States War Department to refrain at this time from publishing the results of these experiments, which had been paid for by the government.[18]

Langley's first trials of his full-sized man-carrying aero-

[18] Charles M. Manly, Discussion of Alexander Graham Bell's paper, Washington Academy of Sciences, *Proceedings*, Vol. VIII (March 4, 1907), 432.

drome were due to start soon after Chanute wrote this letter
to Merrill. Chanute and the entire scientific world as well
were interested in the outcome. But Wilbur marked up another grudge against Langley—he had not yet received an invitation to witness the trials. However, the brothers also took
note of the treatment which Langley was receiving at the
hands of the press, and even this early noticed that the newspaper accounts were obviously misleading.

Langley was, in fact, being hounded by reporters, even
though he had made a definite agreement with the War Department that the public and the press be excluded from the
tests of the aerodrome.[19] The grant of $50,000 from the Board
of Ordnance and Fortification enforced secrecy on Langley,
but the press resented his silence. The papers accordingly
published fantastic stories about Langley's work and built up
expectations that could not possibly be fulfilled. The first trial
did not come off until October, but early in September, Chanute wrote prophetically to Wilbur: "I am really sorry for
Langley. He has had more than his share of mishaps, and the
pesky reporters are giving him the reputation of a bungler."

While Langley was making his final preparations on the
Potomac, the Wrights were starting for their fourth season at
Kitty Hawk. History thus obligingly furnished a dramatic
situation in which the two protagonists were in glaring contrast: Langley, foremost scientist of the nation by reason of
his position as secretary of the Smithsonian Institution; the
Wright brothers, as unknown to the press and the public as
any other bicycle mechanics in any town in the Middle West.
Both were preparing for final tests after years of hard work.
Success or failure? The next six months would show which
was to be their reward.

[19] *Ibid.*

CHAPTER VI

December 17, 1903–Climax and Beginning

THE WRIGHT BROTHERS arrived at Kitty Hawk on September 25. They found, as in the previous two years, that a gale had moved their building—this time, two feet to the east. Instead of rebuilding it, as they planned to do after the usual Sunday observance, they were beguiled by the excellent weather on Monday into practicing gliding.

They made about seventy-five glides in one day and beat their former record by a glide of 30 2/5 seconds. They succeeded also in hovering, once, for 26 2/5 seconds. Hovering was defined by Lilienthal as "stationary flight without forward motion,"[1] and their first success was, Chanute wrote them delightedly on October 7, "great as a beginning and I hope you will next turn a full circle in soaring, as a preliminary to your more ambitious projects."

When they started for Kitty Hawk, they planned to stay there less than two months. But they were delayed by the time consumed in assembling the machine, and then they were tempted by the progress shown by the machine into staying longer. They did not leave Kitty Hawk until late in December, thus stretching the season and increasing the chances of encountering storms and gales. But when they began to assemble the machine, they found their hopes rising and believed that they would surely accomplish a real advance with it. First they completed the upper surface, and happily found that it was far better than anything they had previously built.

Several times, both before and after they went to Kitty

[1] Chanute, *Progress in Flying Machines*, 203.

78

Hawk, the brothers had invited Chanute to visit them, but he hesitated to accept these invitations. The discussions about his article for the *Revue Generale des Sciences* had impressed him anew with their desire for secrecy; he knew their ambitions for this year's work, and realized the possible success they might achieve. But Wilbur urged him to come. Finally Chanute agreed to leave his own business affairs, which caused him some concern this year, and make the effort to visit Kitty Hawk. But before coming, he wrote again: "Do not hesitate to say so if you would rather not have me come."

In the meantime Langley had made his first trial, on October 7, 1903. To the great delight of the press, which had built up fantastic expectations, the machine failed to fly. The whole country, as Mark Sullivan described it, yelled with joy at this proof of the immutability of the universe, of the fact that what had never before been accomplished could never be accomplished![2]

The Wrights' mounting excitement about their own work was heightened by Langley's apparent failure, for it seemed to leave the field open and clear to them. Langley and the Washington group which had slighted Lilienthal had tried—and failed. Now it was up to the Wrights to vindicate Lilienthal and the gliding school—and themselves.

Chanute was eager to see the Wrights' trials, and in the middle of November he arrived at Kitty Hawk, bringing along abundant bedcovers as directed by Wilbur. But Chanute stayed only one week and then had to return to his business affairs without seeing the attempted flight.[3] The new machine was not yet ready to try: first the propeller shaft twisted off, and then the propeller broke.[4] Orville had to make the long 800-mile trip back to Dayton for new parts and did not return

[2] Sullivan, *Our Times*, II, 562 ff.

[3] Chanute, "A History of the Wright Flying Experiments," *Scientific American* Supplement No. 1639 (June 1, 1907), 26262.

[4] Chanute, "Recent Progress in Aviation," Smithsonian Institution, 1910 *Annual Report*, 148.

to Kitty Hawk until December 11.[5] In all, five weeks were spent in fixing the propellers and axles, too long a period for Chanute to wait.

Meanwhile, Langley's machine was given its second and last test on the Potomac. On December 8 it was tried out, and it again failed to fly. The jeering of the press, in Sullivan's apt phrase, "became a kind of triumphant ecstasy of ironic flouting." The newspapers poured a "tornado of ridicule" on Langley, who was the epitome of the comic-strip's favorite scapegoat, a professor and scholar.[6] The reasons for Langley's so-called failure have become an argument which still draws blood. But many scholars agree with Chanute's opinion expressed in a letter written at this time to Thomas Moy:

> The difficulty with Langley's machine was not the lack of stability, but the fact that the launching gear failed him on each of the two? [*sic*] occasions when he tried to fly his machine.

Chanute retained this belief always, and a few years later published a fuller statement in an article about Langley, writing:

> There is no doubt that the apparatus would have flown if it had been launched properly....
>
> It is true that his machine was not of the best type, and that it would probably have been broken at each landing. But it was only by a very small margin that this machine was prevented from being the first powered flying machine to give to mankind the empire of the air.[7]

Whatever the reason, and it may never be settled to the satisfaction of all, the fact is that the hounding and baying of the press misrepresented these experiments, and indeed contributed largely to Langley's death. Langley's tragic experi-

[5] Orville Wright, "Our Early Flying Machine Developments," *The Slipstream*, Vol. VIII, No. 9 (September, 1927), 15.

[6] Sullivan, *Our Times*, II, 565, 567.

[7] Octave Chanute, "Langley, *Son Vie et Son Oeuvre*," *L'Aérophile* (Paris), année 14 (April, 1906), 96.

ence was an object lesson for the Wright brothers. They took it to heart.

On December 14, six days after Langley's final attempt, the Wrights made the first trial of their new machine. There being little wind that day, they started it off from a near-by hill. The machine was in the air only three and one-half seconds, landing a little over one hundred feet from the start. Although two struts were damaged, the machine itself was unharmed. The brothers considered that they had made only a trial on this day, and in spite of the injured struts they found it an encouraging attempt.[8]

It took two full days to repair the struts. The next day, December 17, was most inclement for another trial: winter had set in, there was ice on the ground, and a cold north wind was blowing a gale. But the brothers were tempted to brave the weather because they wanted to get home to be with their family at Christmas.

This desire to be with their family for the holidays was another indication of the Wrights' close family ties. But they were too reticent to acknowledge this reason in their later accounts of this important day. It is unfortunate that the brothers fought shy of giving personal explanations such as this one, for it would have endeared them to the public, which, like nature, abhors a vacuum. They were, however, unable to break through their iron ring of reticence, and they wrote publicly only of their determination to make one more attempt in this inclement weather. They wanted to know whether the machine had enough power to fly, strength to land safely, and sufficient control "to make flight safe in boisterous winds as well as in calm air."[9] Indeed, it took great physical courage, an attribute which the Wrights had already shown they possessed to a high degree, to fly an almost untried machine under such difficult conditions.

[8] O. Wright, "How We Made the First Flight," *Flying,* Vol. II, No. 11 (December, 1913), 35.
[9] *Chicago Daily News,* January 6, 1904.

By ten o'clock on the morning of December 17, 1903, the brothers had made their decision to try their plane. Three members of the Kill Devil Life Saving Station—John T. Daniels, W. S. Dough, and A. D. Etheridge—and two other neighbors—W. C. Brinkley of Manteo and John Ward of Nag Head—composed the gallery of spectators. Orville made the first attempt—*and succeeded in flying!*

Since the brothers themselves wrote an account of this wonderful achievement, their exact words define what this flight of twelve seconds meant:

> The first flight lasted only twelve seconds, a flight very modest when compared with that of birds, but it was, nevertheless, the first in the history of the world in which a machine carrying a man had raised itself by its own power into the air in free flight, had sailed forward on a level course without reduction of speed, and had finally landed without being wrecked.[10]

The exhilaration of this successful flight of twelve seconds impelled them to fly again. Three times more the machine rose, with the brothers alternating flights, as was their practice. On this notable day, Wilbur had the fourth turn and made the longest distance. Years would elapse before any other flyer approached this achievement of December 17, 1903, for Wilbur flew for *fifty-nine seconds* and covered a distance of *852 feet*.

It adds to the excitement of contemplating these first flights to know that they were not perfect. The effort of being born, of emerging into an actuality, was reflected in the straining of the machine and in its erratic undulations. This hand-made craft, carrying its large burden of man's hope and thought, was challenging the hostile elements. The heavy winds increased the problem of controlling the landings, and the fourth flight unfortunately ended in a rough landing which slightly damaged the hard-worked plane.

[10] Wright, "The Wright Brothers' Aeroplane," *Century Magazine,* Vol. LXXVI, No. 5 (September, 1908), 649.

The brothers paused now to contemplate what they had done, and to assess the damage. Worse followed immediately, for while they were standing around the machine discussing the flights with their spectators, a sudden gust of wind hit it and so injured the plane that there was no possibility of flying it again.[11]

These flights on December 17, 1903, were the first controlled flights in history. In spite of the many disadvantages and handicaps under which they had worked, the Wrights had made this extraordinary achievement. One of the best results was that all their calculations, on a preliminary check, seemed to have been absolutely correct.

In the word *controlled* lay their great advance over previous practice and their promise for the future. They had, furthermore, made four consecutive flights. This was not, thus, a chance flight, but a carefully worked out and well-planned feat of the first magnitude.

Enormous elation at achieving one's high goal is inevitably followed by a period during which this success has to be accepted by the mind and absorbed into the emotions. Fortunately, the Wrights had many things to do, and they were kept busy following the fourth flight on December 17, while their minds and hearts and spirits exulted in their achievement. They sent a happy telegram home to Dayton, ending, "Inform

[11] A peculiar contradiction about the injury following this last flight exists in the brothers' writings: Their authoritative account in *Century Magazine* (September, 1908, p. 649) states: "the damage to the machine caused the discontinuance of the experiments." In an article in *Flying* (December, 1913, p. 36), Orville wrote that "all possibility of further flights with it [the machine] for that year were ended." But in another article, in *The Slipstream* (September, 1927, p. 16), Orville wrote, "We estimated that the machine could be put in condition for flight again in a day or two."

The extent of the damage assumed importance when, in 1928, Orville shipped the 1903 plane to the South Kensington Museum in London. There followed a large feeling of regret in this country for the loss of the "original Wright machine." A few voices insisted that the plane had been so greatly damaged after the fourth flight on December 17, 1903, that little was left of the original plane after it had been repaired, and that the loss was, therefore, more sentimental than actual.

Press home Christmas." Katharine Wright immediately tele-graphed to Chanute, sharing the great news with him.

Then came the aftermath, which, as always, was a let-down. The brothers now realized the limitations as well as the promise of their first flights. Although elated at their success, they felt also a slight apprehension lest the shortness of their time in the air overshadow the fact that they had gotten into the air. While they happily considered the events of this great day, occasionally they paused to hope that men who really understood the difficulty of flying a new and strange machine would admire the length of their flights rather than wonder at their brevity. So strong was their feeling that it crept into one sentence of the Wrights' subsequent letter to the press, where they mentioned "the difficulties of attempting the first trials of a flying machine in a 25-mile gale."[12]

On the whole, the world was supremely indifferent to what might be occurring on the sand dunes of North Carolina. Its attention was focused on the many other events of this month of December, 1903: The United States was beginning to stir in preparation for the presidential elections of 1904; Russia and Japan were massing troops in preparation for war. Chicago suffered its second greatest fire. The Dreyfus case was getting under way in France. And in New York City, part of the population was completely absorbed by the opening of the new Williamsburg Bridge, while the other part was focused on the opening performance of *Parsifal* (in the afternoon) and the pulsing question of whether or not to wear evening dress for the occasion.

But the press was not responsible for this indifference on the part of the public, for already, on December 18, the Norfolk *Virginian-Pilot* had broken out in large headlines about the Wrights' flights. On December 19, the Norfolk *Record-Herald* also carried the news. Various newspapers and journals throughout this country picked up these reports and noted

[12] *Chicago Daily News,* January 6, 1904.

them. The brothers were given due credit, although the accounts were distorted: their flights were enlarged into distances of three miles, and their machine was called an airship.

Those interested in aeronautics caught these press reports, and an influx of letters and inquiries poured into Chanute's home in Chicago. Langley, Cabot, and Means in this country, Moedebeck in Germany, and French aeronauts, all wanted to know:

"What have the Wright brothers really done?"

The Wrights, therefore, had to face the question of what to say and what not to say. Although the news had been reported most inaccurately, it had been sent out and noted.

Moedebeck, apologizing for his poor efforts in English, wrote to Chanute: "We are very enjoied about the progress of Mr. Wright. But we know *very few* of the success, only by newspapers!"

Chanute, although irked by the embroidery attached by the press to the actual facts, was delighted with the flights, writing to Cabot on December 19, "I am very much pleased ... with the fact that Americans have been the first to produce a successful flying machine."

He believed that the brothers would now step forth and present the facts of their flights to the public, and, as he was giving an address on the twenty-eighth of December to the American Association for the Advancement of Science, he suggested that the Wrights take this as their opportunity, for, as he wrote them on December 27, "It is fitting that you should be the first to give the Association the first scientific account of your performances. Will you do so? Please wire me."

Chanute was, already, old-fashioned. The Wrights were the new, practical generation and they were headed for the road to financial, not scientific success. They felt that they must be explicit if they addressed the American Association for the Advancement of Science, a foremost scientific society.

Accordingly, once more they refused to give out descriptions of their methods or pictures of their machine.

However, they, too, were irritated by the inaccuracies of the reports of their flights, and consequently at this same time they wrote a long "correction" which they sent to the American press, to the Royal Aeronautical Society[13], and to the French magazine *L'Aérophile*.[14] They also wrote letters to various individuals, including Captain Ferber in France[15] and Major Baden-Powell in England who published it in *Aeronautics, Supplement* to *Knowledge and Illustrated Scientific News*.

The statement to the press gave exact descriptions of their flights of December 17, and is therefore included in full below. It is taken from the January 6, 1904, issue of the *Chicago Daily News*:

TELL HOW THEY FLEW
WRIGHT BROTHERS GIVE ACCOUNT OF AIRSHIP TEST
IN NORTH CAROLINA
SOARED AGAINST A GALE
REMARKABLY FAST TIME IN ONE TRIAL IN TEETH
OF STRONG DECEMBER WIND

(By the Associated Press)

Dayton, O., Jan. 6—Wright brothers, inventors of the flying machine which has attracted such widespread attention recently, today gave out the following statement, which they say is the first correct account of the two successful trials:

"On the morning of Dec. 17, between 10:30 and noon, four flights were made, two by Orville Wright and two by Wilbur Wright. The starts were all made from a point on the level and about 200 feet west of our camp, which is situated a quarter of a mile north of the Kill Devil sandhill in Dare county, North Carolina.

[13] *The Aeronautical Journal* (London), Vol. VIII (April, 1904), 41.

[14] Année 12 (January, 1904), 16–17.

[15] Ferber, *L'Aviation*, 55.

FLIGHT AGAINST THE WIND

"The wind at the time of the flights had a velocity of 27 miles an hour at 10 o'clock and 24 miles an hour at noon, as recorded by the anemometer at the Kitty Hawk weather bureau station. This anemometer is 30 feet from the ground. Our own measurements, made with a hand anemometer at a height of 4 feet from the ground, showed a velocity of about 22 miles when the first flight was made and 22½ when the last flight was made. The flight was made directly against the wind. Each time the machine started from the level ground by its own power, with no assistance from gravity or other source whatever.

LAUNCHED FROM ONE RAIL TRACK

"After a run of about 40 feet along a mono-rail track, which held the machine 8 inches from the ground, it rose from the track and under the direction of the operator, climbed upward on an inclined course, till a height 8 or 10 feet from the ground was reached, after which the course was kept as near horizontal as the wind gusts and the limited skill of the operator would permit.

FAST TIME AGAINST GALE

"Into the teeth of a December gale the 'flyer' made its way, with a speed of 30 to 35 miles an hour through the air. It had previously been decided that for reasons of personal safety these first trials should be made as close to the ground as possible. The height chosen was scarcely sufficient for maneuvering in so gusty a wind, and with no previous acquaintance with the conduct of the machine and its controlling mechanisms. Consequently the first flight was short.

FLIES HALF MILE, 852 FEET HIGH

"Successful flights rapidly increased in length and at the fourth trial a flight of 59 seconds was made in which the machine flew a little more than half a mile through the air and a distance of more than 852 feet over the ground. The landing was due to a slight error of judgment on the part of the navigator. After passing over a little hummock of sand in an attempt to bring the machine down to the desired height the operator turned the rudder too far and the machine turned downward more quickly than had been expected. The reverse movement of the rudder was a fraction of a second too late to prevent the machine from touching the ground and thus ending the flight. The whole occurrence occupied little if any more than one second of time.

DIFFICULTIES IN STRONG WIND

"Only those who are acquainted with practical aeronautics can appreciate the difficulties of attempting the first trials of a flying machine in a 25-mile gale. As winter was already set in, we should have postponed our trials to a more favorable season but for the fact that we were determined before returning home to know whether the machine possessed sufficient power to fly, sufficient strength to withstand the shock of landings and sufficient capacity of control to make flight safe in boisterous winds as well as in calm air. When these points had been definitely established we at once packed our goods and returned home, knowing that the age of the flying machine had come at last.

NEW PRINCIPLES OF CONTROL

"From the beginning we have employed entirely new principles of control, and as all the experiments have been conducted at our own expense, without assistance from any individual or institution, we do not feel ready at present to give out any pictures or detailed description of the machine."

Their phrase, "the age of the flying machine had come at last," was true. Flight was now possible and the Wrights had proved that it was so and had achieved it themselves.

But they did not hasten the coming of the age of flying by helping others to do what they had accomplished, and other men were forced to travel again the same road that they had cut. It was not until 1906, when Santos-Dumont made flights for all the world to see, and was followed by other flyers, that the sun actually rose on the era of the flying machine. The Wrights' flights of December, 1903, could have marked the rising of the sun. As it turned out, this was a false dawn, born prematurely three long years ahead of its time.

The brothers stated their position clearly in the last sentence of their statement to the press, saying "we do not feel

ready at present to give out any pictures or detailed description of the machine." This refusal to publish details of their
work did not mean that they stopped their experiments now.
On the contrary, they continued vigorously and energetically
to develop their "one horse shay" as Chanute called it, so that
it was stronger and could safely achieve longer flights. Even
if the brothers had stopped after 1903, their names would still
have gone down in history along with the names of Lilienthal,
Chanute, Langley, Maxim, Bell, and other pioneers in aviation. But that would not have given them a financial return
on their work.

From this time, indeed, the brothers were determined to
find a way of obtaining a money return on their machine.[16]
They finally decided to give up their bicycle business; their
first success had given them the courage to abandon this regular, although dwindling source of income. They were in no
need of money. They had already refused Chanute's and
Langley's offers of help, and now they received an offer from
Samuel Cabot of Boston, which was likewise refused. Cabot's
suggestion was sent to Chanute in a letter on December 22,
1903, in the following graceful phases:

I suppose the Wrights will have no trouble about getting all the
money they want for further experiments but I am interested
enough to help if any obstacle should occur in the way of "Progress
in Flying Machines" [the name of Chanute's famous book]. I look
upon you and Lilienthal as the most eminent ancestors in this successful effort.

The Wrights described their decision which was made at
this time, and they themselves stated that their expenditures
had not been more than they could afford:

In the beginning we had no thought of recovering what we
were expending, which was not very great, and was limited to
what we could afford for recreation. Later, when a successful

[16] Chanute, "A History of the Wright Flying Experiments," *Scientific American* Supplement No. 1639 (June 1, 1907), 26262.

flight had been made with a motor, we gave up the business in which we were engaged, to devote our entire time and capital to the development of a machine for practical uses.[17]

In France, the commercial possibilities of the airplane had been considered almost as soon as the possibility of flying itself. Ferber sold one of his machines in 1903 and thought that the Wrights were also going to develop this market of individual sales. Immediately on receiving their letter of December 28, Ferber offered to buy a Wright plane.[18] As he remarked, the automobile had been developed in France in the years from 1890 to 1901 by a similar process: men who had little capital made one or two automobiles and sold them easily to individual purchasers.

But the Wrights had other plans and pursued their own way, refusing Ferber's offer. In turn, Ferber described somewhat harshly the general reaction that followed the first wave of joy at hearing of the Wrights' success:

> But the Messrs. Wright . . . became possessed of the idea that they should be, first of all, remunerated by an enormous sum.
> . . . From this moment on, they were enveloped in complete mystery, which gave the world the impression that they were a phenomenal American bluff.[19]

Not until 1908, five years later, did the Wrights finally prove to the world that they were not *"un bluff américain phénoménal."*

A blanket of silence enveloped the brothers after their statement to the press, lifted only for an occasional glimpse of their activities. From this time on, they were, actually, pioneering. They were engaged from now on in their real work, for which their flights of December 17 were the first step.

The Wright brothers were starting the aviation business.

[17] Wright, "The Wright Brothers' Aeroplane," *Century Magazine,* Vol. LXXVI, No. 5 (September, 1908), 650.
[18] Ferber, *L'Aviation,* 55 (German edition, p. 77).
[19] *Ibid.*

CHAPTER VII

"Of What USE Is a Newborn Baby?"–1904

THE WRIGHTS' exultation about their first flights in no
way diminished their realization that much remained to be done before they actually mastered
the art of flying and developed also their flying
machine. Their hard realism and great practical sense helped
them immeasurably to face the coming year—a year of hard
work tinged by deep uncertainty about the future. Although
they were not in need of money, still they had to find a way of
making their living, and since they had now given up their
small bicycle business, their hopes centered on their airplane.

Chanute continued to receive many inquiries as the news
spread through aeronautical circles that the brothers had actually flown in December. One cable from France asked for
further details about their flight of 119,548 meters! He was,
accordingly, anxious to know exactly what the Wrights
wished him to say.

Chanute was surprised when he learned that nothing more
than the January press statement would be issued until later
in the year. This was a change of policy, he wrote to Wilbur
on January 20, for he remembered their telling him in the
previous November that they would give their "performance,
if successful, all the publicity possible." Nevertheless, he sent
the newspaper statement to his correspondents all over the
world, including Hargrave in New South Wales, Moedebeck
in Germany, Ferber in France, and Wenham in England.

Chanute noted the particular sentence in the statement
which said, "But all the experiments have been conducted at

our own expense, without assistance from any individual or institution." He underlined the word *any* and with great frankness wrote to Wilbur, "Please write me just what you had in your mind concerning myself when you framed that sentence that way."

Chanute failed to get a clear answer to his question. He knew, as well as the brothers, that they were already being described as "Chanute's pupils," and that people believed that he had financed them, for Chanute's generosity to inventors was well known. Chanute knew also that the purpose of this phrase in their statement was to correct, obliquely, these impressions.

In addition, the brothers wished to make it clearly understood by this phrase that their work had a different basis from Langley's. Since they, and they alone had paid for their work —the $50,000 government grant to Langley always assumed large proportion in the Wrights' eyes—they felt that they had the moral right to keep their achievements, or rather their methods of achievement, secret.

Having mentioned this clumsy sentence, Chanute did not again refer to it. But the episode rankled. Moreover, the continued hostility to Langley, who was sorrowing for his apparent failure, offended his great scientific generosity.

On their side, the Wrights continued to be irritated by the statements of their intellectual and financial indebtedness to Chanute. They never failed to emphasize their independence of his help and influence. Only a few months before Chanute died, in 1910, did they make any attempts to clear up this ill feeling between them. Other subjects distracted their attention from this personal matter, and on the surface the relationship was a friendly one, with frequent exchanges of amusing and amused gossip as well as discussions of the more serious aspects of aeronautical developments.

At the beginning of this year, Augustus M. Herring reappeared on their scene, in a long letter written to the Wrights as soon as the news of the December flights was reported. Herring said that, while he did not know the exact construction of their successful flying machine, he was sure that it was similar to his machine. Their claims might clash on several points, Herring pointed out, and they might become involved in long and expensive litigation. To avoid this he suggested that they form a company together—he to have one-third interest, and they to have two-thirds. This suggestion, he was sure, would be to their advantage as well as his own.

Wilbur did not take this as a serious threat to their pending patent applications, but was angry, although not surprised, at Herring's impudence. Chanute, however, was concerned about the possibilities of future complications, and more regretful than before that he had taken Herring along with him to Kitty Hawk.

"I am amazed," he wrote to Wilbur on January 14, 1904, "at the impudence of Mr. Herring in asking for one-third of *your* invention. While I could wish that you had applied for patents which I first urged you to, I think that your interests are quite safe. The fact that Mr. Herring visited your camp, in consequence of circumstances which I subsequently regretted, will certainly upset any claims which he may bring forth. I suppose that you can do nothing until an interference is declared. If it is, please call on me, and in the meantime try to find out who is his Patent Attorney."

The Wrights made no reply to Herring's letter, for they did not expect any future trouble from him. Herring continued for many years to be active in aviation; but the lawsuits he threatened in 1904 (and which Chanute foresaw) were started six years later by the Wrights against him. And they did not call on Chanute.

Herring next appeared in the early 1904 issues of Moedebeck's magazine, *Illustrierte Aeronautische Mitteilungen,* with claims that he had started the practice of gliding independently of and simultaneously with Lilienthal; and that he was, as well, the pioneer of many other aeronautical inventions. Chanute took steps to inform Moedebeck about Herring, and wrote him on May 6, 1904:

. . . your New York correspondent [Carl Dienstbach] has been misled into giving first class notices to Mr. Herring in the February and March numbers. I may say to you confidentially that Mr. H., having seen the Wright machine through my own fault, has been engaged in an attempt at "Chautage," by threatening to interfere with the Wrights in the patent office.

Another kind of danger to the Wrights began at this time with the appearance of faked interviews and articles. In general, the Wrights pursued a policy of disregarding them. Chanute wrote them of "a clever piece of 'Journalism' by which you are made to appear to have given an interview to the Chicago Chronicle. . . . You are lucky to have the plans of your machine made for you by the newspapermen."

At this same time *The Independent* (in New York) published an article allegedly by Wilbur, which was actually made up of newspaper reports combined with excerpts from Wilbur's speeches before the Western Society of Engineers. Chanute was enraged, for he was president of the Society, and he wanted to sue the author of the article. But Wilbur was content to force the magazine to acknowledge that the article was published without his consent or knowledge, and was firmly against taking legal action. An important factor in his decision was that Wilbur doubted whether the author was sufficiently responsible financially to make it worth such an action.

The security of their position in having achieved flight and the superiority of their machine were both threatened in still another way, although the threat was as yet no larger than a small cloud on the horizon. In France, the seeds of interest planted by Chanute's talk of April, 1903, had begun to sprout and small shoots of effort were appearing. Those energetic Frenchmen who were to center aviation progress in their work had begun to make their initial efforts to fly. Their journals spurred them on, urging them not to copy American progress servilely, but to strike out on new lines. "This," remarked Chanute, "may lead to further progress, providing that nobody gets hurt."

Captain Ferber, encouraged by Chanute's speech and its aftermath to continue his work in aviation, made careful studies of the Wright glider and worked on his own heavier-than-air machine. At one of his speeches early in 1904 he was sought out by a young man who begged for an introduction to Ernest Archdeacon in order to help develop the art of flying.[1] This was Gabriel Voisin, who soon became the chief designer and constructor of the gliders tried out this year by Archdeacon.[2]

The gliders achieved a small success, Voisin gliding once for five seconds. To improve them, Archdeacon called in Captain Ferber. With his advice they then tried to build a motored plane. This was not successful, and later in the year Voisin left Archdeacon and started with his brother the famous Voisin Brothers firm, which became one of the foremost companies in the world.

Archdeacon's interest and enthusiasm in aeronautics became important factors in its development in France. With M. H. Deutsch de la Meurthe, he then founded a prize to be awarded by the Aero Club de France for a flight of one kilometer over a closed course. (Deutsch, wealthy promoter of aeronautics, and a founder of the Aero Club de France, had given the balloon prize won in 1901 by Santos-Dumont.) The Deutsch-Archdeacon prize dangled until 1908, when it was won by Henry Farman.

When it was first announced, early in 1904, Chanute called it to the Wrights' attention. He cautioned the brothers "to keep your eye on this prize and to perform the feat before

[1] Adams, *Flug*, 96; Ferber, *L'Aviation*, 103.
[2] Lougheed, *Vehicles of the Air*, 140 n., 153.

official witnesses so as to obtain affidavits establishing a record."

Archdeacon's experiments and his belief in the future of the aeroplane received widespread notice and aroused public interest in flying. An interview such as the following could not fail to arouse the public's curiosity. It was first carried in the Chicago *Record-Herald* of March 20, 1904, from St. Cloud, France, and then in the New York *Press*. Chanute, an inveterate newspaper reader and clipper, sent the *Press* notice to Wilbur, who decided scornfully that the description given below was excellent—of Archdeacon's machine!

"The aeroplane has come to stay," he said. "Chanute and Herring, improving on the unhappy Lilienthal, obtained results which encouraged Wilbur Wright and his brother to undertake what have turned out such brilliant experiments. Nothing could be imagined simpler than the Wright aeroplane. It is like this:"

(Here M. Archdeacon drew a rough plan that looked like a man on his stomach at the door of a chicken coop.)

Another Frenchman who had also begun to experiment was Robert Esnault-Pelterie. His machines in 1904 were gliders made like the Wrights', and his purpose was to verify the statements about the Wrights' glides. He was so skillful that his results came very close to those obtained by the Wrights in their first year of work.[3] Esnault-Pelterie went on to develop a powered monoplane which later achieved great distinction.[4]

The Wrights were aware of the great and growing activity in France and followed with interest the many efforts and experiments. But they adhered to their resolve to keep complete silence about their work.

One of the most powerful reasons for secrecy was the question of their patents. They had filed applications in the United States, Great Britain, France, Germany, Belgium, Austria, and probably in Russia, although they were not sure about the last. Until at least some of these had been granted, they

[3] Chanute, "Artificial Flight," in *Pocket-Book of Aeronautics*, 308.
[4] Zahm, *Aerial Navigation*, 337.

would withhold "all information," Chanute explained to Hollands in England, "concerning their experiments with a motor machine."

Chanute passed on the same news to Moedebeck in Germany who was always eager to get anything about the Wrights into print, saying, on February 3, 1904, "the Wright brothers have closed their mouths, and those of their friends since their success. They propose, later on, to prepare an account, but not now."

Throughout the winter and spring the brothers worked on the results of their 1903 flights and their plans for a new machine. They intended to give exhibition flights in various places during the approaching summer season. This was a sound plan, for exhibition flying was to become a highly popular and profitable business. Later the brothers changed their plan and, indeed, felt scornfully that exhibition flying was a circus business where the flyers were merely mountebanks risking their lives for the amusement of the crowd! At this time, however, exhibiting was one of their several plans and served to focus their work.

An immediate opportunity was offered by the aeronautical competition announced for the St. Louis Fair of this year. The brothers considered entering the race and even went to St. Louis to study the fairgrounds and the conditions prevailing there. Because of the rules of the competition, they found the course a very difficult one, and believed that it might even be dangerous if a flyer had to make a forced landing. They were not yet ready to enter the contest formally; in other words, to pay the entrance fee. They would decide definitely after they had tried out their machine again in actual flight. Then they would know whether they would win. For, they reasoned hard headedly and practically, they would compete in order to win, not with the idea of seeing how near to winning they could come. For many reasons, Chanute, who was on the Fair committee, hoped that they would finally decide to enter.

They were not going to Kitty Hawk this year but intended to set up their machine in a field owned by Mr. Torrence Huffman, located about eight miles east of Dayton. There they could be near their workshop.

Furthermore, they were building three planes. These were heavier than the 1903 machine, but of the same size; their engine was going to be geared up, and they expected to achieve a speed of forty miles per hour. By building three machines, with all the parts interchangeable, they would be secured against elimination in the St. Louis contest—in the event of an accident or breakage the parts could be easily replaced. This was admirably astute planning, and the Wrights possessed the energy to carry it out.

By the beginning of May the brothers were almost ready to try out their machine. Again, as in the previous years, their father's church troubles delayed them, and they had to make a trip to Huntington. But soon, they hoped, the first trial could take place, and Wilbur cordially invited Chanute to see it.

At this point the brothers were fully decided to continue their work in secret. Indeed, Wilbur realized with joy that they had not been troubled at all by the press, and that doubtless the reporters had no idea what was going on. "I am glad to see," Chanute replied on May 26, "that the newspapers have not found you out." On this same day, however, all the newspapers of Dayton sent reporters to Huffman Prairie to witness a flight by the Wright brothers—at the invitation of the Wright brothers!

While it is generally a pleasure to find an impetuous act committed by these rigidly conservative brothers, this particular one had unfortunate results. The act itself seemed highly out of character. Why did the brothers, who had avoided publicity, who always based their claims on what they had done

Wright brothers' flying field near Dayton, 1904

Flight of twenty miles in thirty-three minutes, 1905 (Wright)

SANTOS-DUMONT

and not on what they expected to do, why did they now invite
the press to witness a flight in a machine that they had not yet
tried out?

According to their own description the brothers notified
every local newspaper that they would fly on May 26. They
invited the press to be present on this day. And they requested
"only ... that no pictures be taken, and the reports be unsensa-
tional." This was a naïve conception of the operations of the
press. Their reason for these provisions in their invitation was,
they said, that they did not wish "to attract crowds to our ex-
periment-grounds."[5]

The event turned out to be a fiasco, Hamlet without the
ghost. The wind was only three to four miles an hour; the
engine would not work; and the machine refused to rise into
the air. This failure was witnessed by about fifty people. The
next day a few journalists returned again. And again the engine misbehaved, and the machine glided only about sixty
feet.[6]

The brothers had cause, remembering the press's harsh
cruelty to Langley, to be grateful for the gentleness with which
their real failure was treated. Although some papers wrote
about an "airship," they generally gave accurate accounts of
the day and emphasized the effort rather than the failure. The
Chicago Tribune headlined its account:

TEST OF FLYING MACHINE IS
DECLARED A SUCCESS

The *New York Times* printed a two-paragraph dispatch
from Dayton, the first paragraph of which read as follows:

FALL WRECKS AIRSHIP

ON TRIAL IT WENT THIRTY FEET AND DROPPED—

INVENTORS SATISFIED, THOUGH

(Special to the New York Times)

Dayton, O. May 26.—The Wright Flying machine, invented

[5] Wright, "The Wright Brothers' Aeroplane," *Century Magazine,* Vol. LXXVI,
No. 5 (September, 1908), 649.
[6] *Ibid.*

by Orville and Wilbur Wright, brothers, of this city, which made a successful flight at Kitty Hawk, North Carolina, last December, had another trial near this city today, which the brothers say was successful. Great secrecy was maintained about the test, and but few witnessed it.

In all ways this was an unfortunate affair. The Wrights were discredited in the eyes of the press, a fact which they realized when they wrote later, "The reporters had now, no doubt, lost confidence in the machine, though their reports, in kindness, concealed it." The brothers thought that the press was indifferent to their 1904 attempts because the reporters did not know the difference between airships and flying machines.[7] But the terminology of the time was vague. And, indeed, there had been a surfeit of so-called failures, and the Wrights' efforts on May 26 and May 27 were merely the latest in a long series. Possibly the most regrettable feature, however, was that when the brothers later claimed to have flown in 1904, their only witness was Chanute—and his visit did not occur until five weeks after this fiasco.

One good result, temporarily, was that the papers had not aroused inconvenient curiosity in the public, and although it was now generally known that the Wrights were working near Dayton, they were immune from what Chanute called "premature publicity." At any rate, the brothers continued to work on their machines in privacy.

Through May and June they continued to work with the idea of entering the St. Louis Fair, in the preparations for which Chanute was very active.

The star of the contest was to be Santos-Dumont, who was coming to the Fair with a new airship. On him rested the hopes of the Fair's management, for the aeronautical competition was not proving successful. About ninety men indicated that they would enter, but only five (and those did not include the brothers, who did not yet wish to enter formally) had paid

[7] *Ibid.*

the entrance fee of $250. The fact that Santos-Dumont was going to fly was counted as a great drawing card.

"The management feels that it must increase the gate receipts and that no attraction will be so great as that of Santos-Dumont," Chanute wrote to A. Lawrence Rotch in Boston, founder and director of the Blue Hill Meteorological Observatory. "It agreed to pay him $2,000 for extra expenses getting ready for the Fourth of July flight."

Santos-Dumont arrived late in June with a new 60-horse-power engine for his airship, and was given many interviews and much publicity. But he did not fly, after all, and was forced to return to France to repair his damaged balloon. The St. Louis Fair was languishing, Chanute wrote sadly. Wilbur was not surprised that the competition was a failure. He had always believed that the rules were too difficult. But Orville had not agreed with him (this was indeed rare); Orville believed that the people who offered prizes had the right to make the conditions, and entrants had no right to complain since they had not been obliged to enter the competition in the first place.

The aeronautics contest of the Fair was a failure. Only eight men finally paid their entrance fees. No new ideas were brought forward, and the machines showed no advance over previous practice. The greatest attraction—Santos-Dumont— did not appear. What might have turned out an equally great attraction—a public appearance of the Wright brothers—also failed to materialize.

The brothers never even filed their entrance application, and for a very serious reason. They were having at this time, as Chanute wrote in June to Samuel Cabot, "very indifferent success" with their new plane.

Not until August did the brothers really make progress in their flying practice. Their season was a long one this year, lasting from May to December, but there were many difficul-

ties to overcome before they achieved this year's purpose—
to fly a circle.

In the first place, their Dayton field was not, as Chanute
had pointed out, as favorable for flying as Kitty Hawk. This
was a true prophecy, for the weather was variable, winds were
light, and there were frequent calms. The 100-acre meadow
was swampy and was covered by hummocks, and on the north
and west it was edged with trees. In addition, they had unwelcome guests in the shape of cattle and about a dozen horses.
The livestock showed greater curiosity about their activities
than the human population evidenced and constituted a
hazard to their flights.

Chanute cautioned them against running into a cow and
was seriously fearful of accidents this year. But the Wrights
felt that they must master these unfavorable factors and must
learn to fly under varying conditions. They could not always
have the ideal conditions that prevailed at Kitty Hawk. That
these brave men never pampered themselves is conclusively
shown by the awesome boldness of their plans: to fly a circle,
and to do so under unfavorable conditions.

All through July they ran into trouble with the plane, although the engine was highly satisfactory. As in the 1903
flights, the plane showed an undulating motion, which they
hoped to correct by shifting to the back the center of gravity.
They moved the water tank, engine, and operator to the rear
of the machine, and when this was unsuccessful, they remade
several of the parts and hoped that this would serve as a correction. The brothers' patience and attention to details were
particularly marked this year, when they were beset with
technical difficulties in addition to bad weather. Heavy rains
alternated with extreme calms.

Although they did not in this year eliminate to their satisfaction the peculiar motion of the plane, they began to make
better flights in August. By the end of the month they had increased their straight-line flights to a record distance of 1,432

feet. This was the longest possible distance in their field. It was a fine record, but they were not satisfied, since it fell short of their objective—to make a circle. For this next step they needed a faster start than they could get from the usually low winds prevailing at their grounds. In order to become independent of the winds for their initial impetus they began to construct a new device which would give them a fast and reliable start.

"I feel gratified that you are approaching a success, for I feel confident," Chanute wrote on August 14, with his usual hearty encouragement, "that once you get a good start you will make a phenomenal flight."

This was true, for they could rely on their machine and their engine would now give them a speed of forty-five miles per hour, faster than they desired at this time. The new starting device was first tried on September 7, and once more their calculations were exactly correct—the device worked perfectly. The twentieth of September marked the completion of their first circle, an achievement in control and skillful manipulation. The distance covered was about 4,800 feet.

Their great progress was indeed phenomenal. But they were ambitious for longer flights, as shown in a letter written at this time by Wilbur to George A. Spratt:

Our own experiments are progressing satisfactorily and we have had more practice during the past month than in all the rest of the season. We have gotten now so we can fly clear round the field and return to our starting place. So we make longer flights and do not have so much handling to do. We have not had any very long flights yet but as soon as we feel sure everything is just as we want it we will try a *five mile trip*.

. . . We are not showing the machine nor letting the public know what is going on.[8]

In spite of the intention shown in the last sentence above,

[8] U. S. Circuit Court, Western District of New York, III, 818 (letter dated October 18, 1904). The italics are mine.

the news of their work was spreading, and Dayton began to evidence an irritating inquisitiveness about Huffman Prairie. In direct proportion as the word leaked out, the brothers determined to keep absolute secrecy about their machine. But they feared they would have to stop their experiments, and Chanute was urgently invited to come to Dayton before their flying season ended.

Fortunately for the brothers' claims made the following year, Chanute did come to Dayton. On October 15 he saw a flight by Orville which covered 1,377 feet in 23 4/5 seconds. Chanute described this flight in a letter written years later to James Means of Boston saying:

He started up from level ground with a little assistance, gradually rose to a height of about 15 feet and swept a circle to the left at 39 miles per hour. His apparatus, however, tilted and he had to land. One wing striking the ground first the machine was broken, as was not uncommon during the development stage of 1904.

Although the damage was so extensive that it took a week to make repairs, Orville was not hurt. It was another of their many achievements that neither of the brothers had ever been injured in a flight.[9]

In the following year the Wrights began to claim that they had achieved many flights in 1904. With few exceptions, the world was inclined to doubt them, and they were saved from the extremes of disagreeable ridicule only by the fact that Chanute had paid this visit and was willing to come forward and add the weight of his prestige and reputation to their assertions.[10] It was unfortunate this this one flight which he saw ended in an accident, for the brothers continued to make great advances in flying during the next several months.

[9] Chanute, "Artificial Flight," in *Pocket-Book of Aeronautics*, 306; "A History of the Wright Flying Experiments," *Scientific American* Supplement No. 1639 (June 1, 1907), 26262.

[10] *Scientific American*, Vol. 106 (June 8, 1912), 518.

In spite of their worry at the possibility of uninvited witnesses, they kept on practicing flying.

The record of the year was a flight on November 9 when they circled the field four times and covered a distance of over three miles in five minutes, four seconds. They had gone out to the field that day to celebrate the presidential election of Theodore Roosevelt. This was one of few times when political events or, indeed, any happenings in the world besides aeronautical impinged on the Wrights' consciousness. The fact that they were celebrating was in itself noteworthy, although their method of celebration was a postman's holiday, doing just what they would have done in any event. This holiday, however, marked a great achievement, for flying four circles and covering three miles was prodigious. Thus, already by November, 1904, the Wrights could measure their flights in miles, not in feet, and in minutes instead of seconds.

Their range of activities was still bounded by their family, the church, and their flying machines. While this narrowness of interests did not make for a full life, it was nevertheless a great help for their purpose. The Wrights were never diverted from their main road; they knew of no pleasant bypaths on which to linger and were therefore never tempted to loiter there. This was fortunate for their chosen careers, for their energies focused entirely on their aims.

The brothers continued to make notable flights until December and then, with winter far advanced, put the machine away. Their great achievements in this year were well summarized by Chanute in an exultant letter written the following year:

In 1904 it [the machine] was rebuilt with modifications. *105 landings were made,* the best of them preceded by flights of about three miles, consisting of four complete circles over a 100 acre field. There were some breakages in the machine but *no personal accidents.* Flight after flight was made, the longest in 5 minutes and 4 seconds, without any damage to the machine. In November a load of 50 pounds was added (iron bars) and *in December 70 pounds were carried in addition to the operator.* It was found that in quartering flight some changes in the arrangement of surfaces were required and that the appliances for control could be improved.[11]

While the required changes were not perfected until the fall of 1905, the 1904 season had been one of phenomenal records: no personal accidents in as many as 105 landings; circles; actual flights reckoned in miles and lasting for minutes while other experimenters were still thinking in terms of feet and seconds; and, possibly the most important of all in view of their future success, the addition of extra weight.

In spite of this remarkable progress, the Wrights were perplexed by other problems. Indeed, nothing was simple for them as they carved out their aviation business. They were not at all sure of what their next step would be. Although they finally had their machine, they were now beginning to wonder what they would do with it. Possibly they had heard the story told about Benjamin Franklin after he witnessed the first ascent of a man-carrying balloon. This was in Paris, in October, 1783, when Pilatre de Rozier rose in a captive balloon built by the Montgolfier brothers. On being asked whether he thought this new device would ever serve any purpose, Franklin replied: "Of what USE is a new-born baby?"[12]

The Wrights were encountering some difficulties with their patent applications. The German Patent Office was not yet willing to grant their patent; the United States Patent Office suggested in November that they reword some of their claims, and in fact it was not until 1906 that the Wrights finally received their basic American patent. An encouraging aspect at this time, however, was the fact that both France and Great Britain had allowed them patents in March, 1904.

[11] Chanute to the English pioneer, F. H. Wenham, in a letter written on November 24, 1905.
[12] Lougheed, *Vehicles of the Air,* 70

At this moment of indecision the British War Office shed a ray of light on the obscure question of what to do with their plane. It intimated this year, according to a letter from Chanute to Wenham in Great Britain, "that it would take up the invention when sufficiently developed."

This doubtless came through Colonel J. E. Capper of the British Royal Aircraft Factory, who had been at the St. Louis Fair and who then visited the brothers in Dayton.[13] On returning to London, he reported mysteriously to the Royal Aeronautical Society that he expected news to come soon from the United States of a successful powered glider.[14] This was only one of a series of "discoveries" of the Wrights which was to recur through the years. Many individuals all over the world constantly discovered their work and always announced mysteriously that new facts were soon to be divulged.

Other possibilities besides the vague interest of Great Britain began to open before the brothers. The rules for the Deutsch-Archdeacon prize of $10,000 were announced, and Chanute believed that they could win it easily if they would go to France. But that had to wait on their other plans, which were not yet settled.

Then another idea was suggested by Chanute: how would they like to go to Japan? "I have been thinking it not unlikely," he wrote on December 26, "that you should be called upon to go to Japan. It could well afford to give you and your brother $100,000 for a few months work in reconnoitering. Santos-Dumont would preferably be called upon by Russia, as that country follows the French lead.

In short, governments were already beginning to nibble at this new weapon which had just barely begun its existence. Even in this country, which was then so isolated from the belligerency of European powers, some individuals realized the potential value of the airplane in war. Godfrey Cabot, brother

[13] Charles R. Flint, *Memories of an Active Life*, 245.
[14] *The Aeronautical Journal* (London), Vol. IX (January, 1905), 2–3.

of Chanute's friend and correspondent Samuel, wrote in January, 1904, to Senator Henry Cabot Lodge proposing that he urge the United States Government to purchase an airplane for national defense.[15]

But the Wrights were still firmly entrenched in Dayton, and this talk of going to France or Japan, or anywhere further than Kitty Hawk, was strangely incongruous. It was more in keeping with their circumscribed lives to visualize them at this time as they were: staying at home, and touching the rest of the world only through Chanute, aeronautical journals, and patent applications.

Chanute ended 1904 with a significant wish for their happiness in the New Year: "I trust that it will not pass without bringing you a material reward."

[15] Lawrence Dame, *New England Comes Back,* 128.

CHAPTER VIII

"A Practical Flyer Having Been Finally Realized"–1905

Orville: "A young man, of about 30, apparently, slight of build, and with a face more of a poet than an inventor or promoter. In countour, head and face resemble Edgar Allen Poe.
Wilbur: "The elder brother, Wilbur, I found even quieter and less demonstrative than the younger. He looked the scholar and recluse. Neither is married.[1]

AN ASTUTE OBSERVER thus described his first impressions of the brothers in this year. Actually, they were thirty-four and thirty-eight years old, and had achieved at this time what Chanute called "a success as well deserved as it is epoch making." The brothers agreed with this view—"A practical flyer having been finally realized," was their description of this year's work.[2]

Their chief energies were not, however, absorbed by the increasing advances in their plane. The brothers wanted to sell it. Their desire to begin to make money was not caused by the lack of that commodity but by their businesslike desire, held since 1903, to make their aeronautical work become a paying proposition.

The newborn baby had grown up. Throughout this year its purpose in life was being clearly defined in their minds. Up to October, however, they continued to work quietly, con-

[1] Brewer, "The Life and Work of Wilbur Wright," *The Aeronautical Journal* (London), Vol. XX, No. 79 (July–September, 1916), 98, 99.

[2] Wright, "The Wright Brothers' Aeroplane," *Century Magazine,* Vol. LXXVI, No. 5 (September, 1908), 650.

tinuing the long process of applying for patents, developing their flying ability, and extending their flights to remarkable distances.

Their choice of a plan having been finally reached, they clung to it tenaciously for the next three years. In the end they had to modify their plans, but in the meantime the two Daytonians had become well known as applicants to foreign governments and subjects of a controversy that raged over the world.

During the first nine months of 1905, there was no indication of the storm of controversy that would break over their heads. Nothing had been heard from the Wrights since their statement to the press in January, 1904, and their failure when they invited the newspapers in May of the same year. But much air had flowed under their plane since that time.

A few of Chanute's correspondents knew that the brothers were making great strides in their flying ability and in the development of their plane, but even the few knew little about these mysterious figures, shadowy and remote even to those who were inclined to believe the increasing rumors. Chanute sent to the brothers many clippings that were beginning to appear, mentioning the Wrights. He called to their attention an article published in the March *Illustrierte Aeronautische Mitteilungen* in Germany by Carl Dienstbach, which described the Wright machine and gave exact data on their flights.

This article seemed to have been compounded from a letter written by Orville to Dienstbach, combined with pictures from Wilbur's last lecture to the Western Society of Engineers. It aroused great interest in Europe and a good deal of discussion. The Viennese aeronautical pioneer, Wilhelm Kress, who had been experimenting with models since the eighteen eighties, was one of Chanute's many correspondents. Kress had known Lilienthal and had warned him of the bad connections in his glider just before Lilienthal's fatal accident.[3] He was much interested in the news about the Wrights and wrote to Chanute about Dienstbach's article, adding, "I myself don't doubt of the success of the Brothers Wright, but the people here ask: who has seen their flights?"

Always ready to back up the Wrights, Chanute replied: "You can say to the doubters of Mr. Dienstbach's account that *I* have seen one of the Wright brothers' flights."

It was France, however, that evidenced most interest in the brothers. This interest grew in direct proportion as the number of experimenters there increased. Although their activity was great, they were still hampered by the lack of a sufficiently light and powerful motor. Captain Ferber's work showed this weakness: on May 27 he tried out his motored plane, but the 6-horsepower engine was too weak to raise the plane from the ground. This feat was accordingly accomplished by means of a wire which pulled the plane into the air. Then the wire was cut, and Ferber flew or glided on to the ground.[4] He was greatly pleased, and wrote of his achievement: "This is the first powered airplane which has made a stable flight in Europe."[5] However, although it marked a great advance, this was not a free flight.

Other Frenchmen were trying to equal the gliding experiments of the Wrights. Archdeacon and Louis Bleriot, with Gabriel Voisin helping to construct as well as to practice the gliders, were trying out gliding experiments over the Seine.

The Wrights were not at all impressed by the activity in France. The state of French aeronautics was very low indeed, Wilbur thought, when even his gliding records were doubted because they were so brilliant.

At the same time, one of the foremost claimants to the crown of first inventor of the aeroplane climaxed a long life

[3] Zahm, *Aerial Navigation*, 214.

[4] Adams, *Flug*, 87; *Scientific American*, Vol. 96 (April 13, 1907), 315.

[5] Ferber, *L'Aviation*, 76.

of work on flying problems. John J. Montgomery of Santa Clara College in California had been working on the problems of flight for twenty-five years.[6] In April, 1905, his latest form of glider was given a spectacular exhibition flight by the professional parachutist, Daniel Maloney. The glider was attached to a balloon, which towed it to a height of 4,000 feet. Then the glider was cut loose and Maloney guided it to the ground, showing, according to an enthusiastic account, "the most absolute control imaginable . . . the most extraordinary and complex maneuvers . . . figure-eight evolutions performed without difficulty, and hair-raising dives were terminated by abrupt checking of the movement by *changing the angles of the wing surfaces.*"[7]

The italicized words read like a description of the Wrights' wing-warping method. As a matter of fact, it has been claimed (but not legally upheld) that the Wrights' construction, which was for normally flat surfaces, was used by them on curved wings and was, therefore, an infringement of the Montgomery patent. It has also been claimed that the subsequent success in flying by other men, including the Wrights' flights of 1905 and Santos-Dumont's in 1906, could be traced to Montgomery's successful glider demonstrated in the spring of 1905.[8]

Montgomery had indeed developed a remarkably stable glider, which was also exceedingly light, weighing only forty-two pounds. His fame has not been commensurate with this great feat of building a machine that demonstrated its equilibrium in such a severe test. His comparative obscurity can be attributed somewhat to the fact that this first success in April was followed a few months later by a fatal accident: Daniel Maloney was killed in July, 1905, during another demonstration flight.

[6] Zahm, *Aerial Navigation*, 251.
[7] Lougheed, *Vehicles of the Air*, 139. The italics are mine.
[8] *Ibid.*, 140 n., 146 n.; Zahm, *Aerial Navigation*, 282; Chanute, "Artificial Flight," in *Pocket-Book of Aeronautics*, 309.

This was the first fatality in aeronautics since Percy S. Pilcher had been killed in 1899 while gliding. Once again the world's hopes faded, and successful flying seemed to the public once more to be a remote possibility.

Montgomery's work had at first impressed Wilbur very favorably, particularly because of the daring and courage displayed by the flights. But when Maloney was killed, Wilbur felt great sorrow at the tragedy, which was increased by his long conviction that such an accident was inevitable. For Montgomery's pamphlet, Wilbur thought, had shown his ignorance of the true facts concerning pressures. Wilbur had realized then the dangers that would result from Montgomery's lack of true knowledge, but had not been able to think of a way of warning Montgomery and Maloney.

Maloney's flights had been witnessed by large and enthusiastic crowds, but the Wrights, intent upon their own experiments, continued their secrecy. It was not the possibility that Montgomery or other American flyers might learn from the Wrights that bothered them so much as the nearly successful French experiments. If the details of the Wright machine were published, the brothers felt, the Frenchmen would be put on the road to success. It was far better, they decided, for the French to build their planes in ignorance of the Wrights' work and then, by trying them out, demonstrate to the whole world how little they really knew about flying. They would never thereafter be able to claim that they had already known all the principles of the Wright machine. In brief, let the French try out their planes—and fail—before they were given the opportunity of learning the successful principles of flight by seeing the Wrights' methods.

Another reason for maintaining secrecy about the details of their machine was that it was not yet completely reliable: they had not yet solved the question of why it had, in some of the previous year's flights, behaved so erratically. They must discover more principles of control.

In spite of the usual winter attacks of grippe, they continued working on their experiments. Chanute, also laid low with the grippe, debated with interest the problem of calculating the amount of power expended in flight by birds. The brothers, planning their 1905 machine, concentrated on improvements and refinements, not on radical changes, for they were sure of the advanced state to which they had already developed it. They concluded that they had already achieved almost the greatest advance possible in dynamic efficiency. Possibly another 20 per cent might sometime be added to the maximum efficiency now attained, but further advance would lie in improvement of details, and in methods of operating, particularly in the operators' skill.

Their object for the 1905 season was, therefore, to obtain more practice. They were reluctant to return to Huffman Prairie, because of the danger of uninvited witnesses. From now on the brothers' great fear was that if their machine were seen, it could be easily copied—or, what would be worse, that a sight of their machine would give the impression that it could be easily copied or improved on! Finally, however, their desire to fly overcame their fear of publicity, and they returned to the field at Huffman Prairie. They hoped, as in 1904, to eliminate the danger of being seen from the Springfield-Dayton trolley line by timing their flights every ten to fifteen minutes in order to avoid the train schedule.[9]

Once more they were delayed by their father's church affairs. This year, however, the General Conference in Michigan settled the trouble, and their father's faction won a clear victory. The other group, considered scoundrels by the partisan Wilbur, was completely routed. That problem was now, to his great relief, completely settled, and their minds and energies were now free for flying.

Their intention this year (and Wilbur did not feel it to

9 Wright brothers, letter of November 17, 1905, to Editor, *L'Aérophile,* année XIII (December, 1905), 266.

be merely a hope) was to take off from their hangar and to fly in all directions—an ambition indicating how far they had progressed. The plane and engine were the same as in 1904, but the wings were rebuilt. They were still using the horizontal position.[10] Although they found that their skill was increasing, they did not make any notable flights until September. Then they believed that they had finally solved the problem of equilibrium and had eliminated the undulating motion evidenced before by the plane.[11]

In the last two weeks of September they began to increase their flights rapidly, and in that fortnight they flew more than they had in the total of all the previous years. For the first time, on September 26, they flew a distance of over ten miles.

In October they increased their records beyond those of September: on the third, they flew fifteen miles; on the fourth, twenty and three-fourths miles. On the fifth of October, they made a flight of thirty-eight minutes, three seconds, and covered twenty-four and one-fourth miles!

In all, there were forty-nine chief flights in this season, of which only seven resulted in damage to the plane. Even more important was the fact that the operator was never injured in the slightest degree.[12]

Against their achievements the efforts of other men were as yet insignificant; not until 1908, for example, did Henry Farman win the Deutsch-Archdeacon prize for a flight of one kilometer in a closed circuit. The Wrights' progress is brought out by the following table showing the highlights of their past three years' work with a motored plane:[13]

[10] Wright brothers, "Our Aeroplane Tests at Kitty Hawk," *Scientific American*, Vol. 98 (June 13, 1908), 423.

[11] Wright, "The Wright Brothers' Aeroplane," *Century Magazine*, Vol. LXXVI, No. 79 (July–September, 1916), 649–50.

[12] Chanute letter to Wenham, dated November 24, 1905.

[13] Wright brothers, "The Relations of Weight, Speed and Power of Flyers," Aero Club of America, *Navigating the Air*. 6–7.

YEAR	TOTAL WEIGHT* (pounds)	LONGEST FLIGHT OF THE YEAR (miles)	(feet)	AVERAGE SPEED (m.p.h.)
1903	745		852	30
1904	900	3		34
1905	925	24¼		38

* Including load.

The red-letter day of October 5 marked their last flight.

Some friends who had been allowed to watch them fly were so excited that they could not keep the news to themselves. The *Dayton Daily News* of October 5 carried an article about the Wrights; the *Cincinnati Post* of the following day copied this notice. The brothers managed to suppress these editions, as well as a sketch of their plane that was in print. Eventually two sketches found their way to France and were published there in 1906, but in the meantime the Wrights had suppressed them at home.[14]

As the flights passed the thirty-minute mark, they could no longer avoid being seen from the trolley. The train schedule coincided with their flights, and the passengers could see them fly. Here was a final danger to their privacy.[15]

Until this time the brothers chose to ignore the growing volume of letters and inquiries, of hints and doubts. Captain Ferber in June had once again written them an offer to buy one of their machines, but they did not reply until October. Now publicity had started, and the Wrights were frightened. They were so badly frightened, indeed, that they dismantled their machine and put it away, without having achieved their goal of making a flight of one hour's duration. Actually they did not again fly until two and one-half years from this October, 1905.

Now they truly possessed a practical flying machine over

[14] Chanute letter to Ferber, November 9, 1905 in *L'Aérophile*, année XIII (December, 1905), 268; Ferber, *L'Aviation*, 88 (German ed. 109–10).

[15] Wright brothers, letter to editor dated November 17, 1905, in *L'Aérophile*, année XIII (December, 1905), 266.

which they were masters. They believed that they had finally discovered the secret of flying and had conquered the problem of flight. While this was their conception of their role, it did not mean that they wished, in 1905, for public acclaim and scientific fame. Without doubt the Wrights could have achieved immediate, world-wide fame by making one publicized flight, or by writing a scientific article for a scientific journal. But they preferred, and actively pursued, privacy, in order to carry on business negotiations.

When the local papers published accounts of the Wrights, the brothers realized that their frail shell of privacy was springing dangerous leaks. Publicity was touching them before they were ready for it, which meant before they had found a cash customer.

The keynote of their sales policy had been settled: it was to sell to a government, and for the purpose of war.

They considered briefly other plans. One was to organize a stock company, as suggested by Samuel Cabot to Chanute, who then, on December 6, 1905, wrote to Wilbur as follows:

A week or so ago he [Cabot] wrote to ask whether you needed financial assistance. I answered that you did not but had talked of organizing a joint stock co. He now writes that this may be floated by Lee Higginson & Co. of Boston, and suggests that you and I should come on for an interview, and a consultation with a patent expert. I have answered that I would submit the question to you, but doubted your readiness to make talk at present. What do you say?

The Wrights refused. Having decided to try to sell to a government, they would reconsider the idea of forming a company in the following spring. They had previously (in 1903) refused an offer from Cabot, and before that, an offer from Chanute. American capital was, therefore, available to the Wrights for many years. Nevertheless, American capitalists have been unjustly accused of a short-sighted policy in permitting the Wrights to go abroad.

That the airplane would be useful in war was early obvious to the Wrights and to Chanute, as well as to other far-sighted inventors. George Francis Myers, for example, in this year applied for a patent on a device for salvaging an aeroplane by means of a parachute. He also applied for, and in 1909 received, a patent for mounting a gun on a plane.

"How near," Chanute asked Wilbur in May, "[do] you conceive yourselves to be from a practical machine which can be used in war."

Fortunately for his peace of mind, Chanute did not ever know how much the aeroplane, to whose development he had devoted his energies, would increase the awfulness of war. From the point of view of his period, the Wrights' plane was already usable for war: They had progressed so far that they were prepared to furnish a plane that would carry two men and enough fuel for a fifty-mile flight—and they could do it immediately.

This was at a time when the world believed that the first successful flight of a powered plane was still to come and was far in the future; when the public had disregarded the Wrights' statement to the press about their 1903 flights[16] and consequently felt that no one had ever made a public, authenticated flight in a plane.

To anyone but Chanute, therefore, this mention of a fifty-mile flight would have seemed ridiculous. But Chanute knew that it was not an idle boast from his knowledge of the brothers' work and of their characters, for they were not ever merely boastful. There is no doubt that the Wrights were prepared to do exactly this, even though no government would believe their claims or buy their plane for several years.

Being so sure of their plane, they thought it obvious that any government must desire this new weapon. Their first re-

[16] See pages 84 ff.

118

buff was, therefore, doubly disappointing—for it came from their own country.

The brothers offered their plane to the United States Government in a letter which their Representative, Congressman Robert M. Nevins, was to present to the President. Nevins became ill, and the letter found its way to the Ordnance Department which, misconstruing it to be a request for an appropriation, promptly refused it. The Wrights were offended: at the misinterpretation of their letter and also at the tone of the refusal, which their later associate, Charles R. Flint, wrote was "snippy."[17] This was the basis of a grudge which they cherished for many years.

The War Department has borne the brunt of the blame since that time for allowing the Wrights' offer to slip through its fingers. But it should be remembered that the Wrights did not intend to demonstrate their plane before it was purchased, but insisted on a contract before it was flown. (The contract was to be contingent upon their fulfilling certain specified feats.) This alone would have rendered their proposal dubious: the Board was faced with an offer of an untried plane made by two unknown men in Dayton, Ohio. It would have found it hard to justify such a purchase to the taxpaying public, which was in a savage mood and skeptical about even the possibility of mechanical flight. For after all, the secretary of the Smithsonian had had, so the press misinformed the country, a catastrophic failure after wasting what were called huge sums of government money. The hue and cry of the mob, for that was the result of the misreporting of Langley's work, not only hastened his death but made it particularly difficult for the next aeronautical inventor to obtain a fair hearing. The public, in later years, has blamed the War Department for its 1905 refusal of the Wrights' offer, but this refusal was an accurate reflection of the public temper at that time.

There was another reason, also, for the country's indif-

17 Flint, *Memories of an Active Life*, 245.

ference to aeronautics: the United States was far removed from Europe in those days and was therefore less aware of the possible uses of the airplane in war. In France and in Germany, for instance, aeronautical circles were closely identified with the armed forces, and the development of the zeppelin in Germany and the balloon in France was obviously for war purposes. European governments were preparing their armies and navies and were cultivating new weapons of war. The Kaiser was even then bellicose and boastful. In fact, the first World War was already brewing in 1905.

In this country, Langley, as well as the Wrights, suffered a rebuff from the government. Langley requested funds from the Board of Ordnance to try out his aerodrome once more. Expressing his hope that the Board would finance another trial, Chanute had written to Langley on May 25, 1905:

I am confident that if the machine had been launched it would have made a good flight. . . .

I hope that the Board of Ordnance will yet make it manifest that it has not been subscribing to a fallacy, by providing more funds to demonstrate that your apparatus can fly.

But this letter and other appeals were in vain; the Board refused to grant funds to Langley, as well as to the obscure but more successful Wrights.

Chanute was indignant at both refusals, but he did not consider that the brothers had been irrevocably turned down. Had they, he asked, approached the War Department directly? Would they object to his "putting a flea in its ear." Influence, in short, was available to the brothers, sufficient to insure them, at least, of a proper hearing. But the Wrights refused, and Chanute on November 29, 1905, reported to Samuel Cabot:

I thank you and Mr. Higginson heartily for the patriotic interest which you take in the Wrights.

There has been further correspondence with the Board of

Ordnance and I get very indignant each time I think of it, but the Wrights do not wish to have a scandal occur at present, as both the British and French war offices have made overtures. I have urged going to the President with the facts in order to save at least prior rights to this country, but the Wrights believe this will do no good.

There was, thus, another reason besides hurt pride for the Wrights' unwillingness to avail themselves of influence at home: soon after receiving their first refusal from the Ordnance Department, they had made a proposal to the British Government, following up the interest it had expressed in 1904. They took this action with clear consciences, for they had given their own country first chance of recognizing the honor of having "conquered the problem of flight." Having been refused, the brothers had regretfully concluded that the United States would not take action on their plane until some other government had bought it first. Further, it had been Wilbur's and Orville's policy for years to sell only to customers who wished to buy their goods, not to try to force a sale.

Having put the blame on this government, the Wrights placed their hopes on the British and then on the French governments. They cherished their grudge against the United States War Department, but they did not indulge themselves in the same feelings about foreign governments, although these acted as slowly as had the United States.

Their decision to sell abroad was accepted by Chanute, but he hoped that the brothers, by their choice of a nation and control of their product, might possibly confine its uses to peace, making it a factor for peace and not for war. He saw some advantages in selling to the British, but added, "If you close negotiations with England I hope that you will find some way of saving our government from any ill results of its present blunder."

The Wrights, more realistic if less sophisticated than Chanute, realized that their product, once sold, could not be controlled by them. At times they were oppressed by the moral implications of which government to choose—but it was turning out to be difficult to sell to any government.

The United States, meantime, was adding insult to injury; the Patent Office was not yet ready to grant their patent, applied for in March, 1903.[18] Not until the following May, in 1906, did they finally obtain it, after making several changes in the wording. The German Patent Office also withheld their patent until 1906, but the Wrights and also Chanute focused their anger on the United States Patent Office for its short-sightedness.

"Our own U. S. patent office," Chanute wrote to Cabot, "is raising difficulties and is, as well as the Board of Ordnance, pursuing the very fatuous policy which drove Hiram Maxim from the country with his inventions."

This referred to further correspondence with the War Department, which had done nothing to increase the brothers' chances there. They requested that Chanute keep this refusal quiet. Always guided by their good business sense, they realized that negotiations with other governments would be impeded if it became known that their own government had refused them.

The brothers were being forced to realize that curiosity about them could invade even Dayton. Charles Manly, Langley's assistant, made a statement in New York before the new Aero Club of America, saying that they had succeeded in flying their planes and had made many circuits of their field. The Commercial Club of Dayton thereupon sent an inquiry to the Wrights asking the truth of these remarkable assertions. The brothers refused to give any information, saying only that they had flown many times. But, Wilbur wondered to Chanute, did Manly have some informer in Dayton, or had he come there himself? Would it be possible to ascertain whether Manly was wearing a mustache around October 1?

[18] Kelly, *The Wright Brothers*, 112.

Because of such incidents and also because governments were moving too slowly, the brothers now felt it necessary to take steps in order to bring their hesitant customers to the point. They first used Captain Ferber as an indirect means. A few days after their record flight in October, they wrote him a letter, apologizing for their delay in replying to his offer to purchase a machine from them, describing their flights, and saying "we can now build machines that are really practical and suitable for many purposes, such as military scouting, etc." The very next paragraph repeated the bait, and added, "It is our present intention to first offer it to the governments for war purposes."

The letter ended with a catalog of their wares, including assertions that were startling to the point of being highly dubious to those who knew nothing of the Wrights' slow, careful labors and many flights:

> We are prepared to furnish machines on contract, to be accepted only after trial trips of at least 40 kilometers, the machine to carry an operator and supplies of fuel, etc. sufficient for a flight of 160 kilometers. We would be willing to make contracts in which the minimum distance of the trial trip would be more than 40 kilometers, but, of course, the price of the machine in that case would be greater. We are also ready to construct machines carrying more than one man.[19]

On receiving this letter, Ferber was elated at being, so he believed, the first in the world to know this sensational news. Being an army officer, and a patriotic one, he took the letter to his superiors in the War Department. They doubted the truth of the Wrights' claims on grounds which were sage, and which many other people were to mention through several years of debate; as reported by Ferber, "If these men have really flown through the air, it would be known. And how can an ordinary captain in the artillery know about it, when

---

[19] Wright brothers, letter dated October 9, 1905, in Ferber, *L'Aviation*, 84–85 (German ed. 106–107); also in Hildebrandt, *Die Brüder Wright*, 41.

even American journalists, who have the honor of being the best informed in the world, are ignorant of this fact."[20]

Ferber accordingly asked the Wrights to furnish proof of their claims, and wrote to Chanute for verification of their letter. At the same time he asked Frank S. Lahm (an American businessman residing in Paris, who was greatly interested in ballooning and a member of the Aero Club de France) to obtain more information about the brothers and their experiments. Ferber described, in his reply to the Wrights, his own promising experiments, thus exerting a kind of pressure to reduce their price, which had not yet been specified.[21]

But the Wrights were shrewd traders, too shrewd to be so easily bluffed by Ferber. They sent him a letter in reply, which is so clever that it is included in full below:

Dayton, November 4, 1905.

Dear Sir,

We have received your letter of October 20th and compliment you thereon. No one in the world can appreciate your accomplishment as much as we can. It is, in fact, a great step forward to progress from the motorless aeroplane, with its easy control, to the discovery of adequate and effective methods for the mastery of the powered plane, which is so ungovernable. After the experiments of men as capable as Langley, Maxim, and Ader, who spent millions and devoted years of time without results, we did not think it possible to be in danger of being overtaken in less than five or ten years. France is, therefore, lucky. But we do not think that this will diminish the value of our discovery. Because, when it becomes known that experiments have been made in France with powered planes, other nations will be obliged to take cognizance of our knowledge and practice. With both Russia and Austria at present agitated, and the Kaiser seeking a quarrel, a general conflagration may burst forth at any moment. No government will wish to be behind the others in the development of its

[20] Ferber, *L'Aviation*, 85.
[21] *Ibid.*, 86; Adams, *Flug*, 87.

flying machines. In order to be ready one year ahead of the others, the sum which we ask for our invention will be found modest.

Although you may be ahead in France, you will wish to buy our discovery, partly to save the costs of your own experiments, partly to inform yourselves of the state of our art among those nations who are in the process of buying from us the secrets of our machine.

Because of these reasons we are willing to reduce our price to the French government to one million francs, the money not to be paid until after the worth of our discovery has been proved in the presence of official representatives, by a flight of 50 kilometers [31.07 miles] in less than one hour. The price includes a complete machine, its speed, surfaces, etc... [*sic*]—instruction of persons in the use of the machine. This instruction will naturally be given in whatever manner is desired.

Respectfully yours,
W. and O. Wright.[22]

Two points in this letter were of particular interest to the world: the Wrights' (asking) price was one million francs ($200,000). Also, their political comment was not well received, particularly in Germany, when they said *"L'Empereur Allemand cherchant noise."*

Their two important letters to Ferber were published in the magazine *L'Aérophile,* and in the books written a few years later by Ferber and by the German writer, Alfred L. H. Hildebrandt. It must be emphasized that these published letters were not exact duplicates of the original letters. But they aroused so much interest that they are important historical facts, whether they are absolutely accurate or not. The brothers did not publicly correct the published letters, although they were angry at seeing them in print. Ferber had made some changes in the letters and had omitted references to himself, but since these two letters are similar to others

[22] *L'Aérophile,* année XIII (December, 1905), 268; also in Hildebrandt, *Die Brüder Wright,* 42.

written at the same time, they must be accepted as substantially correct. At any rate, the very fact that they were published and were not publicly corrected by the Wrights caused them to be important links in the chain of events occurring this fall.

Ferber replied to this second letter of November 4, saying that the French Government could not consider their plane until it had been seen and verified by a commission of French or American "savants," such as, for example, Chanute, Langley, or Rotch. The suggestion that Langley be asked to authenticate their work could not have been palatable to the brothers, who had mentioned Langley specifically in the letter given above.

Chanute meantime had replied to Ferber's inquiry, backing the Wrights' claims in full and explaining that one article had indeed been published but that the edition had been suppressed. Also, the *New York Herald* of November 26, 1905, had had an article about the brothers. Chanute gave Ferber a clever explanation for the Wrights' silence, saying, "The Wrights have followed the example of France which has kept secret since 1885 the progress of dirigible balloons."[23]

The Wrights saw and approved this letter of Chanute's but continued to request that he say nothing about their work. They repeated this when he visited them in November. But on November 20, a few days after he had returned from Dayton, Chanute was released by the brothers from his promise of secrecy. Their other friends had been similarly released because the brothers had decided it was dangerous to suppress authentic information when so many false rumors were beginning to circulate. Although Chanute did not understand exactly how much he was now permitted to reveal, he indicated that he had no desire to increase his prestige or to capitalize his intimacy with the Wrights, and wrote to Wilbur on November 24:

[23] Chanute letter dated November 9, 1905, to Ferber, in *L'Aérophile,* année XIII (December, 1905), 268.

I shall avail [myself] of your leave to no longer keep secret the results of your experiments by advising Wenham confidentially, but will not volunteer information to others.

Wenham was "the pioneer who first advanced a rational Engineering view of the subject," according to Chanute; he was the man who, reading the first paper before the newly founded Royal Aeronautical Society (Great Britain) in 1866, proposed a design for two or more superposed planes; and he was, therefore, the originator of the biplane form used by the Wrights and many others decades later.[24] Wenham was, accordingly, the one man Chanute picked for his confidant, writing him a long, strictly confidential letter describing the progress of the Wrights's experiments and the details of their flights. Generous pleasure was felt by Chanute, aged seventy-three, foremost American pioneer, in being able to write about "the practical flying machine" possessed by the Wrights for the past two years, and, he added proudly, they "have been improving it." His exultation was shared by Wenham, British pioneer, eighty-two years old.

Chanute's letter marked "Private and Confidential," was, however, a great anticlimax. The very next day after receiving it, Wenham saw an article in the London *Daily Telegraph* from France which reported the news of the Wrights' flights and their offer to the French government at a price of one million francs.[25] Evidently Ferber had shown his letters from the brothers to the press—but Ferber claimed that it was not he who had first let the news leak out. Some news had leaked somewhere, and the excitement was great.[26]

Why don't the Wright brothers issue a statement? *The*

[24] Lougheed, *Vehicles of the Air,* 149; Zahm, *Aerial Navigation,* 185.

[25] Wenham's letter to Chanute, dated December 8, 1905. However, the *Automotor Journal* (London), December 9, 1905, p. 1542, said that *L'Auto* (Paris) published the news first in its December 1 issue.

[26] Ferber, *L'Aviation,* 87 (German ed., 109).

Automotor Journal of London asked, adding, "The situation is distinctly silly"![27]

The wish was granted, when the December issue of *L'Aérophile* appeared, containing not only the letters to Ferber from the Wrights and Chanute, but a letter from the brothers to Georges Besançon, editor of the magazine—which letter was written by the brothers for publication!

Three days before they had released Chanute and their other friends from secrecy, the Wrights had written letters to four men in three countries, intending that they be printed. Their purpose was to stir the French and British governments to quicker action. Although their release of Chanute and their friends was thus a hollow gesture, these four letters had an immediate effect. Their four correspondents were chosen with care and skill: they were Georges Besançon, editor of *L'Aérophile;* Colonel J. E. Capper of the British Royal Aircraft Factory at Farnborough; Patrick Y. Alexander, influential member of the Royal Aeronautical Society; and one man in the United States—Carl Dienstbach, friend of Augustus M. Herring and New York correspondent of the German journal, *Illustrierte Aeronautische Mitteilungen.* Thus the brothers passed over all other American scientists and all other American societies.

They could have notified the Aero Club of America, formed in October, 1905; or they could have written to the Fédération Aéronautique Internationale, formed also in this fall and composed of eight clubs (including the Aero Club of America) from eight different countries. They preferred, although Chanute again urged them to communicate with it, not to make a statement before the American Association for the Advancement of Science. They were, indeed, focusing on foreign prospects.

At least two of the four letters were published—one in the December, 1905, issue of *L'Aérophile,*[28] and the other which

[27] December 23, 1905, p. 1601.

is given in part below, in the *Aeronautical Journal* of the Royal Aeronautical Society:

Wright Cycle Co.,
1127, West Third Street,
   Dayton, Ohio.   November 17, 1905.
Dear Mr. Alexander,

                   We have finished our experiments for this year after a season of gratifying success. . . . During the month of September we gradually improved in our practice, and on the 26th made a flight of a little over 11 miles. On the 30th we increased this to twelve and one-fifth miles, on October 3 to fifteen and one-third miles, on October 4 to twenty and three-quarter miles, and on the 5th to twenty-four and one-quarter miles. All of these flights we made at about thirty-eight miles an hour, the flight of the 5th occupying thirty minutes three seconds.[29] Landings were caused by the exhaustion of the supply of fuel in the flights of September 26, and 30, and October 5, and in those of October 3 and 4 by the heating of bearings in the transmission of which oil cups had never been fitted. . . . We had intended to place the record above the hour, but the attention these flights were beginning to attract compelled us to suddenly discontinue our experiments in order to prevent the construction of the machine from becoming public.

The machine passed through all of these flights without the slightest damage. In each of these flights we returned frequently to the starting point, passing high over the heads of the spectators.

If you think the contents of this letter would be of interest to the members of the Aëronautical Society of Great Britain, you are at liberty to communicate as much of it to them as you please.

Hoping that we may have the pleasure of seeing you on your next visit to America,

    I beg to remain,

                        Very respectfully yours,
                        Orville Wright.[30]

[28] Wright, letter to editor dated November 17, 1905, in *L'Aérophile*, année XIII (December, 1905), 266.

[29] This should read 38 minutes, 3 seconds.

[30] *The Aeronautical Journal* (London), Vol. X (January, 1906). Reprinted in Vol. XIII (January, 1909); and also in Chanute, "Artificial Flight," in *Pocket-Book of Aeronautics*, 306–307.

Almost the same letter as the above was published in
L'Aérophile.[31] The latter, however, was signed by both brothers. Moreover it included also a postscript addressed to the
editor Georges Besançon, saying that if he wished to verify
their claims they could refer him to many well-known citizens
of Dayton and also to the members of the Lifesaving Station
at Kitty Hawk. The Wrights did not refer to any of the many
well-known American scientists for the simple reason that
none except Chanute had seen their machine. They rested, for
their international references, on Dayton's citizens.

The editor of *L'Aérophile,* after publishing the above
letter and the other correspondence, then, as he said, indulged
himself in a three-page debate about these communications,
notable because the discussion reflected the opinion of many
in the world. The first question was whether or not to believe
the Wrights. On the whole, the magazine was inclined to
believe them, the main reasons in their favor being their
scientific reputation (based, no doubt, on Wilbur's addresses
to the Western Society of Engineers), and their 1904 letter to
this same magazine. These considerations were heavily but-
tressed by Chanute's well-known scientific achievements and
honesty.

But, *L'Aérophile* continued, why did they offer the plane
to the French Government? Why not to their own government? Was the United States so discouraged by Langley's
failure that it would refuse a machine that was capable of the
flights claimed by the brothers? If it had indeed reached the
stage of perfection they claimed, why had they not found some
American capitalists—*"les plus hardie de l'univers"*—to finance them? Or did the Wrights realize that interest was
keener in France than anywhere else, and did they hope by
these letters to find a French syndicate?

The next question was: Exactly what value did the Wright
machine possess? Several experts were then quoted to the ef-

31 *L'Aérophile,* année XIII (December, 1905), 266.

fect that the Wright machine was merely a more advantageous arrangement of other men's ideas, and a better construction of others' designs; in short, that it did not possess a single new or novel feature.

The argument concluded by a quotation from Archdeacon's recently published advice to the Wrights: They should, said Archdeacon, give their invention to their own government. At least that would insure them of honor and gratitude. If they held out for their fantastic price of one million francs they would lose all chance of getting either money or honor— and he questioned whether they deserved the latter.[32]

This was the beginning of a growing volume of excitement and interest. The brothers refused to answer inquiries from newspapers or to issue statements through them. The mountain was thus forced to go to Mohammed. Strangers began to arrive in Dayton. They tried to locate the Wrights, and succeeded only after some difficulty.

Robert Coquelle, an editor of the magazine *L'Auto,* was sent to Dayton to verify the Wright's claims. After many inquiries Coquelle found the brothers' home through a former bicycle racer. The result of his visit was that Coquelle wrote a complete verification of the Wrights' claims for *L'Auto.* While his account was not accurate, the fact of its publication (as in the case of the Wrights' letters to Ferber[33]) was important, and he was never publicly called to account for his inaccuracies.

Frank S. Lahm cabled to a cousin in Mansfield, Ohio, to go to Dayton. Harvey M. Weaver, the cousin, also failed to find the brothers at first: "I inquired, after a time, whether there was such a firm in the city, but no one could give me any information. There was none in the directory, and no one seemed to know anything about a 'flying machine.' "[34] Finally Weaver

[32] *Ibid.,* 268–71.   [33] See pp. 125–126.
[34] Brewer, "The Life and Work of Wilbur Wright," *The Aeronautical Journal* (London), Vol. XX, No. 79 (July–September, 1916), 97.

found the brothers, went with them to their home and to Huffman Prairie, and then wrote a long letter to Lahm completely substantiating their claims. He wrote also the description of the brothers which heads this chapter.

A few days later Coquelle's cable was received in France: "The Wright Brothers refuse to show their machine. But I've seen the evidence; it is impossible to doubt."[35]

The committee on aviation of the Aero Club de France met to consider the claims of the Wright brothers. The majority, headed by Ernest Archdeacon, and including Louis Bleriot, decided not to subscribe for the purchase of the American machine, since it was not yet perfected, and they hoped that a better one would soon be available. The minority, including Captain Ferber and Georges Besançon, believed that the Wright brothers had produced a truly successful flying machine and wished to obtain for France "the industry or the sport which would result."[36]

A few days later, at another meeting of this committee, Lahm read aloud Weaver's letter, and Coquelle, whose articles were appearing in *L'Auto,* testified that he also was convinced that the Wright machine could fly and had flown. Many members were now persuaded of the truth, but Archdeacon insisted that the Wrights were trying for a promise of one million francs only in order to interest capital for the building of a better machine.[37]

Among those present at this meeting was Alberto Santos-Dumont. An important result of the furor about the Wrights was the fact that it aroused his interest in heavier-than-air flight. Hitherto his great energies had been confined to his airships. In less than a week after this meeting Santos-Dumont filed formal notice of his intention to compete for the Deutsch-Archdeacon prize, first announced in 1904.[38]

[35] *Almanach des Aviateurs pour 1909,* 18; also in *Automotor Journal* (London), December 23, 1905, 1601.
[36] *Almanach des Aviateurs pour 1909,* 18.
[37] *Ibid.,* 18–19.

The Wright brothers had written another letter to Georges Besançon, on December 13, in which they gave the names of their witnesses. The names were, by request of the Wrights, not published. Seeming always to require secrecy, somehow, somewhere, the brothers asked Besançon to withhold the names in order that these important men of Dayton be protected from a deluge of inquiries.

Their letters had had some success, of the kind the brothers desired, in addition to these heated controversies. The British military attaché in Washington, Colonel H. Foster, wrote that he was coming to Dayton to witness a flight. Ferber cabled: "Friend with full power for stating terms of the contract will sail next Saturday, wire if convenient. Ferber."

The brothers answered, economically and laconically, "Time convenient. Wright."[39]

The brothers kept to their decision: Colonel Foster was informed that while the machine had been dismantled, they would be glad to have him make full inquiries concerning their past flights. It would, they felt, place them at a great disadvantage to demonstrate the machine and then try to bargain for terms. The time for bargaining about a contract was, they believed, before the goods were delivered, not afterward.

The brothers had timed their letters well, even though publicity was now beating down on them. The United States indicated in December that their patent would shortly be allowed—the French and British patents, with the same basic claims, had long since been granted.

No matter what the scientists thought about the long history of aeronautics and the Wrights' niche in the procession; no matter whether the press chaffed at their coy silence; no matter whether some thought the brothers niggardly in their disregard of Chanute's helpfulness; no matter that others

---

[38] Brewer, "The Life and Work of Wilbur Wright," *The Aeronautical Journal* (London), Vol. XX, No. 79 (July–September, 1916), 78.

[39] Ferber, *L'Aviation,* 89 (German ed., 112).

would try to demonstrate that the Wrights' devices were hoary with age—the fact was that the brothers would soon possess patents which could be forged into a weapon to control the aviation industry.

On January 3 it was announced that the Wrights had given M. Arnold Fordyce[40] and a French syndicate an option on their machine. This was Ferber's "friend with full powers," who, it was reported, had agreed to a price of 1,000,000 francs, plus 25,000 francs if the option were not exercised within six months. Ferber remarked ruefully on his ability to make so much money so easily for other men, compared with his failure to obtain the small amount required to build his new No. 9 aeroplane.[41]

Now it seemed as though the brothers had succeeded in their objective. But the newspaper reports were exaggerated. The negotiations with the French were not concluded and indeed had just begun. At this moment the Wrights were asking Chanute for advice on the best way of dealing with agents. How could they protect themselves if Ferber's friend was not a representative of the government, but was only negotiating for a commercial group?

The year of 1905 ended with continued secrecy on the part of those Americans who could have given to the world valuable information on how to make a successful flying machine. The impasse was well described in the authoritative book by Zahm:

It was a curious situation; Langley and Manly, who produced the first aeroplane endowed with all the essential powers of prolonged flight, were bound to *official secrecy;* the Wrights, who had a finished machine, tried and fairly ready for public exhibition, were hampered by *trade secrecy.*[42]

[40] *L'Aérophile,* année XIV (January, 1906), 22.
[41] Ferber, *L'Aviation,* 89 (German ed., 112).
[42] Zahm, *Aerial Navigation,* 251.

CHAPTER IX

Selling a Gold Brick–1906

THE YEAR opened auspiciously for the brothers. M. Arnold Fordyce sailed for France with an option on the Wright plane. By August 1 they were to deliver a flying machine on which they would make a demonstration flight of fifty kilometers. The long contract included a clause in which the brothers swore that their apparatus was not a balloon, and that it was truly a heavier-than-air machine.

Fordyce was to deposit 1,000,000 francs with J. P. Morgan and Company in New York by April 5, 1906, and 25,000 francs by February 6, the latter to be paid to the Wrights if the option was not taken up. After a short period following the fulfillment of the terms, the Wrights were to be free to sell to other nations.[1]

Chanute, always hoping for peace, wrote to Wilbur on January 17, 1906, about these terms:

I am delighted to learn that you have sold a flying machine to the French for $200,000, and this, without onerous restrictions as to sales to other Nations.

This may not make for peace as much as an exclusive sale to one Nation for now they will all have a machine, and I fancy that the French have acted so promptly because they expect early war, but it will make you world famous, and eventually millionaires, if you care for the latter. . . .

I hope that universal peace will result.

The plane was intended for the French Army, and the

---

[1] Georges Bia, *Les Frères Wright et Leur Oeuvre*, 43 ff.

War Department participated in the negotiations following Fordyce's return there. The Wrights wrote to Frank S. Lahm a letter of thanks for his interest, and mentioned in it another prospective customer, evidently fearing that the French contract might not go through.

This letter was published in the January issue of *L'Aérophile,* but it did not hasten the French negotiations. The proposal which the Wrights mentioned vaguely to Lahm as coming from a society in "another European country," was actually from an Austrian group that was planning to present a Wright plane to the Emperor Franz Joseph for his sixtieth birthday in 1908. The brothers were hopeful that this idea would spread to other countries. Then they could establish a real aeroplane business. If this eagerly-hoped-for result should occur, they would probably be able to make as much money as they wished, and they felt that they would be satisfied easily. Like all others who have not yet begun to reap an anticipated golden harvest, the brothers were sure that they would be satisfied if only they could have an assured, certain income.

But the Austrian project fell through and the French deal was dubious. Fordyce and his associate, M. Letellier, editor of *Le Journal,* were trying to raise the one million francs. They approached various French capitalists, including Rothschild and Deutsch, and were refused. The price was considered too high, and, a more important objection, too many people doubted the Wrights' claims.[2]

Magazines and journals were still arguing about the mysterious Wrights. Whether or not to believe them accounted for many lines of type. The battle waxed particularly strong in France, and the brothers, ignoring the harm that the skeptics might do to their negotiations, refused to join. Chanute was aware of the danger, and asked Wilbur for explicit instructions as to what he might write about them, withholding other information until Wilbur clarified his release of

[2] Adams, *Flug,* 88; Ferber, *L'Aviation,* 89.

Chanute in the previous November. "Thus far," Chanute wrote on January 17, "I have limited myself to assurances of your perfect truth and reliability."

Wilbur felt that they could not ask Chanute to vouch for the performances of their machine, since he had seen only one short flight in 1904. They had not, therefore, called upon Chanute as a witness for the 1903 and 1905 flights, which he had not actually seen; and they were regretfully forced to forbid him to vouch for what he did know, which was the construction of their flyer.

In France, Fordyce and Letellier, having failed to interest French capitalists, approached the Minister of War, M. Etienne.[3] He was sufficiently interested to send a mission to Dayton for further negotiations with the Wrights. They telegraphed Chanute asking him to come to the conference with the mission and, as usual, Chanute responded.

These negotiations failed; the French asked for a reduction in the price; for an extension of time during which they were to possess exclusive rights to the plane; and requested also that the flight be made at a height of three hundred meters.[4]

The Wrights immediately refused to try for altitude during their test flight, and they would not consider any sum less than one million francs. On their side, they insisted that the experiments be conducted in secret, and steadfastly refused to show their plane before signing a contract.[5] Fordyce said later that Wilbur refused all his requests for even a snapshot showing their airplane in flight.[6]

By the spring of 1906 it was obvious that the deal was falling through. The Wrights' first earnings from their flyer came

---

[3] Ferber, *L'Aviation*, 98; Adams, *Flug*, 88.

[4] Bia, *Les Frères Wright et Leur Oeuvre*, 48.

[5] Chanute, "Recent Progress in Aviation," Smithsonian Institution, 1910 *Annual Report*, 148.

[6] Bia, *Les Frères Wright et Leur Oeuvre*, 45.

from the forfeit deposited with J. P. Morgan and Company—
from a refusal to buy, and not from a sale.[7] The news spread
throughout Europe that the French had turned down the
Wrights. Even worse for their business was the rumor that
their own government had also refused them.

At this same time, Patrick Y. Alexander, British student
and promoter of aeronautical activities since the eighteen
nineties, visited the brothers in Dayton. Chanute hoped that
his trip would bring an offer from the British Government,
"A result," he wrote to Wilbur, "which has commended itself to me from the start." But there were no tangible results
of this visit. Wilbur thought that Alexander had probably
come only to find out for the British Government what the
French had decided to do.

This was a year to try the brothers' souls. They needed
their large resources of resolution, fortitude, and persistency.
Negotiations went up and down like a fever chart. Governments blew hot and then turned cold. They had announced
their phenomenal flights, and the result was disappointing,
inasmuch as their unwilling customers still held off. Half the
world believed them; the other half doubted them, or pretended to do so, in an effort to make them come down on
their terms.

Chanute was encouraging them, saying, "I think you will
readily establish that it is not a gold brick you have to sell, but
that there will be a good deal of hesitancy about the price."
But they were not easily establishing the value of their wares.

In addition, the possibility of a successful competitor was
always present. Their purchasers played up this threat in order
to stave off coming to a conclusive agreement. The Wrights'
friends, fearful that their competitors might win the race
against the slow-moving, deliberate Wrights, urged them to
hasten their negotiations. Still the brothers refused to consider

[7] Kelly, *The Wright Brothers,* 184–85, 189.

the idea of a commercial company. As they wrote to Lahm in January, "We have not yet begun to think of forming commercial companies because we hope to receive sufficient compensation without doing so."[8]

At this time the brothers wanted only a sure income in order to be free to pursue the study of questions which they had as yet touched only superficially and for practical purposes. To assure this desired safety of income, it seemed to them that a sale to a government would be the best solution. They had no wish to form a commercial company or in any way to be a part of the commercialization of their aeroplane. They foresaw clearly the business involvements and patent litigations that would attend a commercial company.

Once more they refused an offer of financial assistance from Samuel Cabot, made shortly before his death. They were, actually, not in need of money, but they were determined to sell to some government. They even wrote, in April, to the German, Italian, Russian, Austrian, and Japanese governments, offering their plane on terms similar to those refused by the French. These efforts brought no results.

The Wrights had offended the Germans by the phrase in their letter to Ferber of November 4, 1905, in which, as translated into French, they had referred to the Kaiser as *"cherchant noise,"* which meant, as Chanute translated it for them, literally "seeking a fuss." Mild as this phrase now seems, it was too strong for the Germans, and Moedebeck's magazine picked up the French phrase and featured it angrily. Moedebeck did not, Chanute remarked to Wilbur, write to him frequently at this time, "probably believing me an auxiliary to the French, which I am not."

When the French deal was lagging, Moedebeck in April wrote to Chanute the following letter, which was typical of what many in Europe believed at this time:

[8] Wright brothers letter to Frank S. Lahm dated January 3, 1906, in *L'Aérophile,* année XIV (January, 1906), 22–23.

I do not believe what pretend the Wright brothers! You have not seen them flying all round and the witnesses the names of them they have now given, are not competent people for me. I am astonished that not one of the given witnesses has written an article in the papers about the grandios effect. . . . Therefore I have said showed your flight before competent people as you, Mr. Chanute, and then make one rapport about the experiments then I will believe it but before never!

Such a machine has after my private opinion no value for warfare. That was a dream! I wish to the Wright brothers that very much nations might purchase their flying machine except the German nation.

Several months later, after the French deal had finally failed, Moedebeck tried to obtain a detailed description of the Wright machine, writing Chanute the following bait and sending a similar letter to the Wrights:

With the Wright brothers invention it is come as I have predicted it. One has delivered their proposition as well at Paris as at Berlin, and what is to do now?

I can only repeat again that the Wright brothers must overthrow their secrecy and I have proposed them to give a clear publication with photos in the Illustrierte Aeronautische Mitteilungen, that the attention of the Aeronautical world might be concentrated again on their experiments, that they will convince "tout le monde," that their pretensions are true. In Germany is nobody today who believes the success of the Wrights, in Austria there are some people who believe what they desire.

In a suave and subtle reply, on July 27, Chanute gave an excellent description of the Wrights' attitude at this time:

I think you are in error about Wright Brothers. They do not desire to draw the attention of the aeronautical world. In fact they deprecate it. They are firmly resolved to publish no photographs or descriptions of their machine, but to let imitators blunder (patauger). They do not propose to exploit their machine commercially but are willing to wait for years until some occurrence makes its use indispensable to those nations which have not already secured it. Knowing what I do, I believe they are right, and I hope that the final result will not be harmful to your country.

Actually, the position of the Wrights was improving, in spite of the French refusal. In May, 1906, the United States Patent Office (which had been notably reluctant to grant patents for flying machines) and then Germany also granted their basic patents, applied for three years before. This delay was one of the many reasons for their secrecy. The Wrights, and Chanute also, were relieved when their basic, famous United States Patent No. 821,393 was finally allowed. Although the patent was a description of their glider, their wing-warping method of control was clearly described, and included in its claims. This was the keystone of their later lawsuits, and the Wrights gave certain warning of the significance they attached to their method of control long before they instituted suits for infringements of patents.

They communicated their claims of flight now, in a long letter to the new Aero Club of America, similar to the letters sent in November, 1905, to the editor of *L'Aérophile,* the Royal Aeronautical Society, and to two other men. This was their first letter to an American group, and it emphasized their means of control, stating: "The favorable results which have been obtained have been due to improvements in flying quality, resulting from more scientific design, and to improved methods of balancing and steering. The motor and machinery possess no extraordinary qualities.[9]

The Aero Club of America verified the Wrights' claims and announced that the Wrights were to be believed. The *Scientific American* also made a check of their claims, writing to seventeen witnesses and publishing the favorable results of its poll.[10]

[9] Wright brothers, Communication to the Aero Club of America, *Scientific American* Supplement No. 1579, "The Wright Brothers' Flying Machine and What It Has Accomplished," Vol. 61 (April 7, 1906), 25303.

[10] *Scientific American,* Vol. 94 (April 7, 1906), 291–92.

Circles in the United States and Great Britain were increasingly convinced of the truth of the Wrights' letters. Alexander Graham Bell and Charles Manly in the United States, Sir Hiram Maxim and Major Baden-Powell (president of the Royal Aeronautical Society) in England, were only a few of the scientists who made public speeches remarking about the Wrights' achievements. But France and Germany continued to be skeptical. France not only doubted the Wrights, but hoped, more eagerly than before, to surpass their (unbelieved) records.

People will not, generally, believe what they have not seen. The Wrights never realized the importance of this psychological fact, which constituted a stumbling block in their negotiations. They even believed that their battle to convince the world of their veracity was ended, after their letters of November, 1905, and the subsequent verifications by the *Scientific American,* the Aero Club of America, and increasing numbers of individual inquirers.

Chanute tried to warn them of the prevalent doubts, having received many letters about them. There were actually many people in the world whose efforts to fly could be seen, and while some were dismal failures, many others seemed to be well within reach of the ultimate goal. The excitement and interest aroused by these efforts should have warned the brothers, but they concentrated on actual achievements.

Experiments were beginning all over Europe. In Denmark, for instance, J. C. H. Ellehammer was experimenting with a biplane.[11] The Prince of Monaco had, for some time past, subsidized aeronautical experiments.[12] In England, S. F. Cody was working on the problem, and in Germany a syndicate was experimenting with aeroplanes. The center of the greatest activity was, however, still in France, where Santos-Dumont, Robert Esnault-Pelterie, Bleriot, Voisin, Levavasseur,

[11] Salmonsen's *Konversationslexikon,* 1918, VII, 111.
[12] *Scientific American,* Vol. 95 (August 18, 1906), 117.

Trajan Vuia, Ferber, and many other men were active. As Chanute warned Wilbur, "Some of them may develop something." Robert Esnault-Pelterie, according to Chanute's opinion, "is the man who is proceeding on the most rational lines." Early in the year Santos-Dumont was building a "screw-flyer" or helicopter.[13]

Competition was indeed becoming keener, and the possibility that someone else might soon achieve a successful flying machine worried Chanute, Cabot, and other well-wishing friends of the Wrights. Besides the possibility of a sale, there were other stakes worth competing for: prizes totalling about $65,000 were being offered in England for the first London to Manchester flight. The Deutsch-Archdeacon prize of $10,000 (first announced in 1904) had been augmented by the $600 Archdeacon cup for the first flight of twenty-five meters (eighty-two feet), and a $4,000 prize announced in this year.[14] But the Wrights did not intend to compete in the open market for these prizes, even though the amounts might seem sufficiently large to attract men who wished only for enough money to pursue scientific studies.

Wilbur grew restive under the proddings of Chanute to make haste in negotiations, particularly when Chanute sent on letters from Paul Renard of Paris and a similar one from Samuel Cabot of Boston saying: "As a business matter however I fear the Wrights will find they have placed their ideas rather high. It seems to me that there are probably several methods that might succeed without infringing their patents and that probably their most valuable asset was their first having done the trick, which they are losing by delay."

The brothers would not be hastened, since they did not feel that they were "delaying"; it was only that they refused to be forced into changing their terms or reducing their price. It

[13] *Scientific American,* Vol. 94 (February 10, 1906), 129.
[14] *Scientific American,* Vol. 94 (February 10, 1906), 129, 136; Vol. 95 (November 3, 1906), 318; (November 17, 1906), 363; (December 1, 1906), 398.

143

was not actually the price that was causing any delay, but the hope cherished by their customers of getting another, equally good plane at a cheaper price. The Wrights felt that they could well afford to wait patiently until the governments themselves discovered that no other plane would be forthcoming. The brothers were sure that no one could equal, much less surpass the Wright machine within the next five years.

They were sure that their reasoning was based on a cold appraisal of the situation, and an application of the law of probabilities. To them the salient fact was that they alone knew the real difficulties of the flying problem. Even Mr. Chanute had little realization of the innumerable problems connected with flying.

In truth, the brothers were harrassed by doubt and worry. Chanute realized the mental strain and stress they were under and sent them on October 15 the following patient letter, which was only slightly tinged with irony:

You are quite correct in saying that it is not the amount of money involved but the possibility of buying your machine cheaper which causes your clients to hesitate. The value of an invention is whatever it costs to reproduce it, and I am by no means sure that persistent experimenting by others, now that they know one success has been achieved, may not produce a practical flyer within five years.

The important fact is that light motors have been developed. As there are many shapes of birds, each flying after a system of its own, so there may be several forms of apparatus by which man may compass flight. Flapping wings for instance.

I cheerfully acknowledge that I have little idea how difficult the flying problem really is and that its solution is beyond my powers, but are you not too cocksure that yours is the only secret worth knowing and that others may not hit upon a solution in less than "many times five years." It took you much less than that and there are few (very few) other able inventors in the world.

It is an index of the large affection the brothers felt for

Chanute that they continued the argument, for their mutual harmony was so great that they very rarely explained their motives to other people. Chanute's letter, given above, did not correctly present their ideas; they did not believe themselves to be superior to Maxim, Bell, Edison, Langley, Lilienthal, and Chanute—who were among the greatest men in the world. Although they stressed the factor of mental ability, they believed that their success was due largely to a combination of circumstances. The law of probabilities indicated that these circumstances, which had not happened to come together before, might not again occur. Indeed, they appreciated the element of chance: it was possible that, if time were turned back six years, they might not again take advantage of the thousand and one factors that had finally totaled up to success. They believed in the "right man at the right time" theory of success, and brought forth the usual argument that a second Napoleon would not now appear if war should be declared, although there were undoubtedly as many able men in the world as in Napoleon's time. Similarly, the chances were 100 to 1 against the successful development of another flying machine in the next five years, no matter how many able men were involved with this problem now.

The Wrights thus understood well the significance of the personal factors that make for success, the imponderables which can never be fully explained by even the most intuitive and conscientious biographer. They relied on their application of the law of probabilities, but kept it in its proper place, using it to bolster their own confidence and to reaffirm their carefully planned course of action.

But Chanute was increasingly concerned by the progress being made in Europe and wrote news that showed how hot the race was becoming. He ended his letter of November 1, 1906, on a resigned note, saying, "I suppose that you can do no better than to await the result, for the outcome will depend not only upon the 'mental ability' which you misunderstood me as constituting the sole cause, but upon mechanical instinct and that conjuncture of circumstances which is sometimes called luck."

Wilbur changed his analogy from Napoleonic terms to a more homely metaphor: the fact that lightning rarely struck more than once in the same place was no reason, they realized fully, for relying on its always keeping to this rule. They had, therefore, not been wasting their time while awaiting a sale, but had been building parts for *several* machines, in order to be ready to give a demonstration flight immediately after signing a contract. They had, in fact, developed a new engine and were planning to build four or five by the coming spring. This new engine was nearly fifteen pounds lighter than their old ones and developed 8 horsepower more.

The Wrights were fortunate in possessing this great quality: they never lost sight of the practical side, even in this discouraging period of waiting and negotiating. It took courage and energy to continue to build and to develop a lighter engine, when their nerves were taut and their course was being criticized. But they never forgot their goal of making a sale, and in the midst of building their new engines, they tried out various means of pushing their proposals. In near desperation they decided that they would even, if they had to, go to Europe. They had no wish to leave their home and no desire to make personal contacts with government officials or in any way to push themselves forward personally. Going to Europe was their last resort.

Nevertheless Chanute was apprehensive for his friends, and in several letters showing his fear that they could, and would, be surpassed, he urged them not to "rest upon your oars." He warned them, "It is practice, practice, practice, which tells and the other fellows are getting it."

As if to sharpen Chanute's proddings, the world was electrified by the appearance, once again, of Santos-Dumont. His interest in heavier-than-air flight having been aroused by

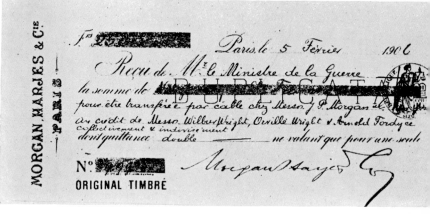

Option check from the French government

Curtiss *June Bug,* July 4, 1908

GLENN H. CURTISS
at the Grande Semaine d'Aviation de Champagne, 1909

the meeting at the Aero Club de France to consider the news from the Wrights, in December, 1905, he decided to experiment in this field. In an incredibly short time he achieved a signal success, for by August, 1906, Santos-Dumont was ready to fly—and in a heavier-than-air machine.

Santos-Dumont started to experiment with a helicopter, but soon changed to a cellular type of biplane.[15] His engine was the remarkable "Antoinette," produced by Levavasseur, who was also beginning to develop his Antoinette plane with the help of Captain Ferber.[16] Santos-Dumont first tried out his new biplane in July when he towed it from his airship No. 14, thereby giving it the name of "14-*bis*."[17] By August 22 he was ready to dispense with the airship, and on that day he tested the 14-*bis* at Bagatelle, skimming back and forth across the field. The plane rose off the field several times in the course of these runs.[18] Some authorities have called these the first flights in Europe; others believe that they were merely brief hops.

A short while after these first successful efforts by Santos-Dumont, the Danish aeronaut and inventor J. C. H. Ellehammer on September 12, 1906, rose briefly from the ground.[19] Ellehammer became an excellent flyer, but Santos-Dumont had preceded him in rising by a matter of only a few weeks. There were many others who were nearing the goal at this same time.

By September 13, Santos-Dumont's plane was ready for a real trial flight. After several attempts, Santos-Dumont actually made a short flight. It lasted a few seconds and covered from fifteen to twenty feet. There was no doubt, this time, that the 14-*bis* had flown. Ernest Archdeacon, head of the Aero Club commission which witnessed the flight officially,

[15] Chanute, "Chronology of Aviation," Smithsonian Institution, 1910 *Annual Report*, 160.
[16] *Scientific American*, Vol. 95 (December 22, 1906), 471.
[17] Adams, *Flug.* 97.
[18] *Scientific American*, Vol. 95 (September 1, 1906), 153.
[19] Salmonsen's *Konversationslexikon*, VII, 111.

announced that this was the first public flight in France of a motor-driven, man-carrying, and entirely free aeroplane.[20]

But this important "first" was only an exciting beginning. In a little over a month, after making a few structural modifications in the plane, Santos-Dumont on October 23 flew a distance of about two hundred feet. He thereby won the $600 Archdeacon cup, which had been offered for the first flight covering eighty-two feet (twenty-five meters). Actually, he had covered the required distance more than twice.[21] This flight aroused great enthusiasm, although the press as usual stretched the actual accomplishment, reporting that Santos-Dumont had covered one kilometer, or five-eights of a mile.

Now, it seemed, Santos-Dumont was pressing hard on the Wrights' heels. He was a very present danger to their unique position. Chanute felt that his warnings were being unfortunately fulfilled and with an overtone of worry wrote Wilbur that not only Santos-Dumont but other men in France were creeping up on the Wrights' records. About Santos-Dumont he wrote on November 1 as follows, indicating clearly that if Santos-Dumont had already progressed to where the Wrights had been in 1904, then his rapid progress might soon reach their present level:

I presume that you have seen in the "Aerophile" for Sep. and in the "Aeronautical Journal" for October (just received) that Santos Dumont made a short flight on Sep 13th, and that the press dispatches say that he won the Deutsch-Archdeacon prize on the 23d of October, by flying over one kilometer, coming down with a bump. I fancy that he is now very nearly where you were in 1904. He seems to have found out that the dihedral angle of the wings, which Langley used, is unsafe in side winds and he is putting on flexible tips. He may hereafter meet with a serious accident and he may not.

[20] *Scientific American*, Vol. 95 (October 6, 1906), 250; Brigole, *Santos-Dumont*, 65.

[21] Zahm, *Aerial Navigation*, 257; *Scientific American*, Vol. 95 (November 17, 1906), 363.

Once more the Wrights were fortunate in their objectivity. For very cogent reasons they were not disturbed—even though Santos-Dumont was obliterating the Wrights from the memory of the world. They had actually progressed incomparably further than Santos-Dumont even approached at this time; for they had made, as they had written to the Aero Club of America, 160 flights and had covered almost 160 miles. Why, then, should they be concerned about a flight which, as Chanute had written, "came down with a bump"? It was easy, they knew to *jump* a plane for a distance of even 250 feet, and Wilbur was willing to prophecy that the official reports would show that Santos-Dumont had not covered over one-tenth of a kilometer. Wilbur was right.

With legitimate self-confidence the brothers were willing to define the exact place at which they would begin to be concerned about Santos-Dumont's competition: When he had made a flight of over three hundred feet, and when he made a landing in a seven- or eight-mile wind.

Santos-Dumont worked much faster than the Wrights expected. Within a few weeks, on November 12, he made several flights, each longer than the previous ones, the longest covering 722 feet (220 meters).[22] Being now ready to attempt a circle, he again formally entered the competition for the Deutsch-Archdeacon prize of $10,000.

Flying machines could fly! The large crowds at Bagatelle were frenzied with excitement; the news spread throughout the world. It was Santos-Dumont who, three long years after the Wrights' first flights, proved this tremendous fact to the enthusiastic world. He had, it seemed, really inaugurated the era of flying. As he had done in 1901 and previously, so in 1906 Santos-Dumont once again captured the world's imagination and aroused its interest in flying.

The Wrights were eclipsed. Although Santos-Dumont's flights could not compare with those of the Wrights—who

[22] Zahm, *Aerial Navigation*, 257.

had turned circles in 1904 and had flown over twenty-four miles in 1905[23]—his flair and his personality caused their claims to be forgotten.

In Dayton still, the Wrights were bolstered by the knowledge of their superior records. Slowly they realized the importance of Santos-Dumont's work and felt that it was an advance over the previous work in France; indeed, they considered it was the first real advance shown there in five years.

Santos-Dumont's personal charm was so great that he exerted what an English writer has called "an almost mesmeric influence on mankind"[24]—truly a contrast to the quiet Wrights. Important as were his actual achievements, even more important was Santos-Dumont's influence on the world. A. F. Zahm described the effects of his flights in 1906 in the following exact words:

> Intrinsically the achievements of November 12th were crude and primitive; but in moral effect they were very important. They marked the inception of public aëroplaning before the professional and lay world alike. There was no patent mechanism to conceal, no secret to withhold from rivals. . . . If Santos-Dumont was not the first to fly, he was the first aëroplane inventor to give his art to the world, and to inaugurate true public flying in the presence of technical men, as he had initiated modern motor ballooning. His liberal enthusiasm and that of his colleagues, both aeroplanists and patrons, quickly made France the world's foremost theater of aviation, at least for the moment.[25]

Santos-Dumont was once more the center of interest and now began to be hailed as the first man to fly publicly in a heavier-than-air machine. His flights, in contrast to those of the Wrights, were well authenticated, having been witnessed by officials of the Aero Club de France and also by large crowds.

[23] See pp. 115–116.

[24] Bruce, "The Aeroplane Experiments of M. Santos-Dumont," *The Aeronautical Journal* (London), Vol. XI (January, 1907), 19.

[25] Zahm, *Aerial Navigation*, 258.

They were called the first public and successful flights of a powered plane in the world.[26]

Unfortunately, chauvinism has seen to it that each nation desires the label of "first to fly," and Brazil, Santos-Dumont's native country, cherishes a grudge still against the United States because of the Wrights' claims of prior flight. This feeling has increased through the years and has impeded the progress in Brazil of the harmony between that country and the United States, a harmony vitally essential to both.

When, in 1940, President Franklin D. Roosevelt designated December 17 as Pan American Aviation Day, Brazil became so angered that the government considered filing an official protest against this neglect of its claims on behalf of Santos-Dumont. All private planes in Brazil were actually grounded in protest on December 17, 1940.[27]

All evidence underlines the truth of the Wrights' claims that they had first flown three years before Santos-Dumont's brilliant success in the fall of 1906. But Santos-Dumont's flights were the first public flights to be believed immediately by the world at large; therefore, they were believed to be the first public flights in the world. Now we have the wisdom of hindsight, and believe that the Wrights flew first in 1903. But if time were set back to the fall of 1906, we, too, would feel that the age of flying had just been inaugurated before our eyes—and by Alberto Santos-Dumont.

It seemed therefore, at that time, that his were the first public and successful flights of a powered plane. This belief prevailed in spite of the verification of the Wrights' claims which had just been announced by the *Scientific American,* the Aero Club of America, and by various scientists.[28] This official and scientific support of the Wrights was forgotten

[26] *Scientific American,* Vol. 95 (November 3, 1906), 318; Lougheed, *Vehicles of the Air,* 148; Dienstbach, Introduction, Aero Club of America, *Navigating the Air,* xxxix.

[27] *The New York Times,* November 24, 1940; December 18, 1940.

[28] See pp. 141–42.

and Santos-Dumont was, once again, the hero of the hour, and his achievements of this fall were hailed in heroic terms.[29] In truth, the current of excitement that circled the world at the news of Santos-Dumont's flights marked the beginning of the age of flight. For the world now really believed that man could fly.

As the end of 1906 drew near, events seemed to be moving slowly in the Wrights' favor. The terms they had been trying to get seemed finally to be within their reach: Ulysses D. Eddy, representing Flint and Company, visited them on Thanksgiving Day.[30] The result was a visit to New York to talk over the terms of a contract with Flint.

The brothers timed their trip so as to coincide with the second Annual Aero Show, and to be in New York at the same time that Chanute was there. From New York they went on to visit Washington. There they met some of the Smithsonian staff, and were modestly surprised to find that Professor Zahm and Dr. Bell were particularly pleasant to them.

Unfortunately, this trip to Washington was too late for them to meet Langley. Langley had died in February, amid general sorrow and, what would have been very hard for that proud man to bear, pity for his disappointment. Wilbur, who had never agreed with Langley's scientific methods, shared in this pity for Langley's so-called failure. At the time of Langley's death, Wilbur believed that his machine would probably have flown. The large condition he attached to this belief was: *if* it had started. Even though the brothers believed it would possibly have been wrecked on landing, they felt that the probable flight would have given Langley the honor he had tried so long to obtain. With gratitude the brothers recalled

[29] *Aerial Age* (New York), Vol. II (September 27, 1915), 29; October 18, 1915), 102; *Ibid.*, (January 10, 1916), 397; J. Armengaud, jeune, *Le Problème de L'Aviation: Sa Solution par L'Aéroplane*, 85.
[30] Flint, *Memories of an Active Life*, 246.

their debt to Langley for his advice, and even more, for the encouragement of his example.

As the methods used by the brothers differed from Langley's, so did the conditions under which they worked. Langley was a public servant, paid for his experiments by the grant from the War Department. Although he was as reticent as the Wrights, he could not avoid the publicity that attended his prominent position. The Wrights, alone and unknown, worked for years before they would even demonstrate their plane in a flight. They kept their experiments within their own means, being able in this way to retain their independence of thought and of action.

Langley, too, refused private financing after that first failure of his career in 1903. His reason was high patriotism and did not spring from a fear of being obligated to his backers. His work had been financed by the nation, so Langley reasoned, and was, therefore, for the nation. If his country no longer supported his efforts, he would not take with him the knowledge gained for it to a private undertaking. But the nation, influenced by the disgraceful treatment accorded his work by the press, would not grant funds for another attempt.

Langley's friends all agreed that his death was hastened by his keen disappointment over this refusal of the Board of Ordnance to finance another attempt at launching the aerodrome. Chanute, who had known Langley for many years, wrote to Baden-Powell after Langley's death, saying: "I feel very sorry for Langley's disappointment and death. When I last saw him a year ago, he was a stricken man. The stupidity of the Board of Ordnance, in refusing to try another launch, killed him."

The Wrights' attitude toward the press was greatly influenced by the shabbiness with which it had treated Langley.

On their return to Dayton from this trip to Washington, the brothers had a definite offer from Flint to think over: The main point was a price of $500,000 for the rights, excluding the United States, which the brothers kept in their own control. Although the offer was satisfactory, the brothers did not immediately commit themselves, being held back by moral and ethical considerations.

Before accepting the terms they inquired of Chanute about Flint's character. It was a feeling of moral responsibility that made them pause. They believed wholeheartedly, it must be emphasized, that theirs was the one and only successful aeroplane in the world. Further, they were equally positive that this unique invention would be used for war by the first government to buy it. They were, therefore, the moral guardians of this new weapon.

These ethical considerations had long been felt by Chanute. He had, he replied on December 22, 1906, known Flint for twenty-five years, but had had no business relations with him. He thought Flint was a very rich merchant, "who has had extensive dealings with the South American Republics and with European War Departments."

At the same time Chanute reported another possibility:

The terms and price ($500,000) which he offers you seem better than I thought possible, but there remains the moral question of what precautions should be taken if the invention passes into the hands of a single nation.

That Government, I believe, would be Russia. I wrote a letter November 17th to Mr. Georges Berthenson, a Surgeon attached to the Aeronautical Park at St. Petersburg, in which I gave an account of your performances and now have his letter of Dec. 1st, in which he says that he has recommended your machine to his Government. Its purchase may mean a new war against Japan and much bloodshed.

Nothing came of this maneuver. And the negotiations with Flint, like their previous ones, also began to lag. Once more they were faced with a doubting customer. This time it was doubt of the value of their patents which held up the contract. Flint and Company was trying to decide whether the Wrights' superior experience and knowledge, plus their priority in the field, would give sufficient grounds for the exploitation of the Wright plane.

Flint was not going to rely entirely on their patents, which might be of questionable value. Indeed, he considered that reliance on patents alone was poor business practice on the grounds, he wrote later, "that patent litigation was expensive, in the end generally unsatisfactory, and that it was not popular, as aggressive patent litigation interfered with the natural evolution of the art."[31]

Again a New Year arrived, with the Wrights in possession of their secrets and their plane, but without a signed contract. The world was beginning to forget them. Even the *Scientific American,* after publishing its verification of the Wrights' flights, in six months forgot that they had flown in 1905. In an editorial reproving Santos-Dumont for, of all valuable things in the world, his exuberant optimism, the magazine said:

In his enthusiasm the Brazilian aeronaut forgets also that at least three experimenters in America (Herring in 1896, Whitehead in 1901, and Wright brothers in 1903), Maxim in England (1896), and Ader in France (1897), have already flown for short distances with motor-driven aeroplanes, and yet no really practical machine of the kind has as yet been produced and demonstrated.[32]

After these years of effort, the brothers were still in Dayton with their machine, empty handed. Writing letters, negotiating, and waiting. Not flying, for they had had too much publicity to again take the risk of being seen. They did not chafe at staying in Dayton, having, indeed, never had any wish to leave their city. But they wanted to come to some settlement, and to have their affairs in order. Lacking contact with the

[31] Flint, *Memories of an Active Life,* 253.
[32] *Scientific American,* Vol. 95 (November 24, 1906), 379.

world outside of Dayton, they had sought to avoid worldly involvements. Slowly they became involved in what was happening in aeronautical affairs, particularly in France, and were gradually pushed to a realization of their own stake in world events.

Through Chanute's correspondence and their own increasing circle of acquaintances, they came in touch with aeronautical developments. They began to meet other aeronauts who came to Dayton: Captain Thomas S. Baldwin, the balloonist, accompanied by the man who made his engines. This was Glenn H. Curtiss, and he, too, visited the Wrights.[33] They discussed the rumors of experiments with wireless, and Wilbur knew that Curtiss was preparing a motor for Alexander Graham Bell's aeronautical experiments. Flying and building airplanes had not yet begun to engage Curtiss's interest further than the building of engines.

This meeting in 1906 of three quiet men brings to mind the now famous Curtiss-Wright Company which later linked their names. Before this Wall Street marriage, however, they became the foremost opponents in American aviation, facing each other in the law courts as bitter enemies. This enmity was more in keeping with their characteristics than the later intertwining of their names, for already in 1906 these young men were carving out their careers. The granite determination of the Wrights had shown itself in the past few years, and is particularly revealed in Wilbur's face.

Curtiss pursued his objectives with equal determination. Up to this time he had focused on motorcycle racing and motor building, but soon after this meeting with the Wrights in Dayton, Curtiss became associated with Bell, and through him and the Aerial Experiment Association started to make his contributions to the art. Curtiss had a forceful personality, and his name became known over the country in a few years. One air-struck young girl of the next generation of flyers was given

[33] Kelly, *The Wright Brothers,* 288.

an added urge toward trying to fly when she passed him on the street and recognized him. After many years had passed, his piercing eyes were what the famous flyer, Katherine Stinson, remembered first about Glenn H. Curtiss.

The Wrights had other visitors in 1906 besides Baldwin and Curtiss. Harvey Weaver came to see them again, bringing along his cousin, Frank S. Lahm,[34] who had presented Weaver's letter about the Wrights to the stormy session of the Aero Club de France the year before. Lahm's son, Frank P., had recently started his accumulation of honors by winning the first International Balloon Race. With Major Henry B. Hersey he had achieved the feat of flying the *United States* from Paris to London.

The horizons of the Wrights were stretching. They had been as far away from home as New York and Washington. Europe was coming closer to them.

[34] *Ibid.*, 192.

CHAPTER X

Curtain Raiser–1907

ROM NOW ON these home-loving Daytonians were forced to travel far from Dayton, and in spite of their attachment to their home town, they continued to travel for the next five years until Wilbur's death. Desiring to keep out of the world's busy highways, they were, nevertheless, forced into contact with its worldliest aspects: Hart O. Berg of the Browning gun and the Lake submarine companies, Charles R. Flint of Wall Street, and European war departments engrossed them this year.

But they were able, for this one year more, to continue to keep their activities quiet. This was not wholly advantageous to their negotiations, for the fact was that the public had all but forgotten them. Toward the end of the year it seemed that their hush-hush policy was succeeding too well, for the work being done by other men drove the Wrights' claims out of the memories of their customers and the public alike.

Aero clubs were springing up like mushrooms, in this country and in Europe.[1] Many of them featured ballooning contests; but all of them were formed by men and lads who had decided that they must, somehow, fly. Some of the clubs were headed by men like Professor H. LaV. Twining in Los Angeles, who worked on his ornithopter all night with boys who were his physics students during the day at the Los Angeles Polytechnic High School. Out of this club came, for instance, Warren S. Eaton, who was to build remarkable

---

[1] Octave Chanute, "Recent Aeronautical Progress in the United States," *The Aeronautical Journal* (London), Vol. XII, No. 47 (July, 1908), 52.

planes in a few years. But in 1907, possessed of little knowledge and less equipment, they were all moved by a high enthusiasm to do the impossible, that is, to fly.

Like the Wrights when they started eight years before, many of them believed that there was no prior art or previous literature on the subject. Many never became acquainted with the already large bibliography of aeronautics, but started out by themselves, and through their own efforts achieved a certain familiarity with the problem of flight that stood them in good stead when they became famous exhibition flyers in a few years. Others, more studious, became familiar with the history of aeronautics, and combined with their reading a practical application that eventually produced important contributions to the art.

To the latter there was available early in 1907 an article written by the Wright Brothers for *Navigating the Air,* a book published by the Aero Club of America. This article, entitled "The Relations of Weight, Speed, and Power of Flyers," by Orville and Wilbur Wright, was two pages long and contained exactly what the title specified, recounting without any elaboration the improvement in their engines and planes from 1903 to 1905. But the last paragraph of this slightly dull, factual article, must have amazed those boys just beginning to try to fly, and, equally, may have impressed those older men who had spent years in vain attempts to get off the ground.

For the Wrights calmly ended this unexciting account with the statement that it was now, "even in the existing state of the art," an easy matter "to design a practical and durable flyer that will carry an operator and supplies of fuel for a flight of over 500 miles at a speed of 50 miles an hour."

Consider that no one in the world had made a flight before the public of even one thousand feet; that the Wrights' longest claimed flight (which they had not wished the public to witness) was a little over twenty-four miles; and that a prize had just been offered for the first public flight in the United States of one kilometer, or five-eights of a mile (and the Wrights did not try for this prize). And yet the brothers quietly asserted that it was now possible to fly five hundred miles.

It is likely that the Wrights could have performed this "easy matter," for they always understated, when they stated anything. But their verbal challenge went unnoticed, for men were too busy with their efforts to turn a circle and to fly short distances with some degree of control and certainty. There was a yeast working which would soon bring forth exhibitions and contests, and would usher in the heyday of individual, exhibition flying. Two aviation magazines were started in 1907 in this country: *The American Aeronaut and Aerostatist,* published in St. Louis; and *The American Magazine of Aeronautics* (later to become *Aeronautics*), edited by Ernest LaRue Jones in New York City. All these and many other ventures were started at this time, moved by enthusiasm and hope.

The United States Government, too, was beginning to show its first interest in heavier-than-air machines since 1903, when it had ended Langley's experiments. Already in April of this year Wilbur was dickering with the War Department. In June, Orville, at the Board of Ordnance's request, offered it a Wright plane for $100,000. But the Wrights doubted that any positive action would be taken by this government, and continued with their other plans. Also, they still cherished their grievance over the War Department's refusals to consider buying their plane, and so would not take any steps which might expose them to another rebuff.

Chanute, while fearful of the old-fogyism and ignorance of aeronautics that might be displayed by the War Department, nevertheless offered his help to the Wrights in forwarding the interest that Washington was beginning to show in their work. He wrote to Wilbur on May 2, "If I were not afraid of interfering with your plans and wishes I might easily stir up the U. S. War Department." But Wilbur continued to focus his efforts on European governments, and Chanute did not "stir up" anything.

Both Chanute and the Wrights were insufficiently aware of the current activities of the War Department, for in July, 1907, the army established the Aeronautical Division of the Office of Chief Signal Officer. In order to keep abreast of current experiments, it sent Major George O. Squier on a tour of foreign air centers, and assigned Lieutenant Thomas E. Selfridge to Nova Scotia to observe Alexander Graham Bell's promising aeronautical work.[2]

In the broader aspects of aeronautical problems, the United States showed itself at this time to be more advanced than other nations. At the Second International Peace Conference held at The Hague from June to October, 1907, the United States delegates signed a declaration prohibiting the discharge of projectiles and explosives from balloons. Finally this country was the only first-class power to sign this agreement.[3]

Actual flying progress was limited largely to France, where many experimenters were making successful although short flights. So great was the interest in flying in Europe that many Americans were concerned about the apparent lack of progress here, and some were inclined to blame the Wrights for this state. James Means, editor of the *Aeronautical Annuals* of the eighteen nineties, expressed this feeling in a strong letter to Chanute, saying:

I tell you that owing to the Wright Brothers having kept so mum all these years the Europeans are getting ahead of us! Someone over here has got to do some hustling.

The Frenchmen were (if they are not now) years ahead of us on the automobile. Shall it be the same with the aeroplane?

[2] U. S. House of Representatives, 70 Cong., 1 sess., Military Affairs Committee, Hearings on HR 11273, April 3, 1928, "Pioneer Aviators," p. 5.

[3] George O. Squier, "The Present Status of Military Aeronautics," *Journal* of the American Society of Mechanical Engineers, Vol. XXX (December, 1908), 680–81.

Means, and others who felt as he did, had cause for concern. Issy and Bagatelle were crowded with men making daily efforts to fly. They were trying out monoplanes as well as biplanes, helicopters, and ornithopters. Santos-Dumont, always busy with new ideas, was working on what one magazine described in quotation marks as " 'an hydroplane,' and with this he hopes to skim the surface of the water."[4]

In March, Leon Delagrange (a sculptor) first tried out the biplane built for him by the Voisin brothers. Bleriot, having separated from Voisin, began to build his own planes. He achieved only short flights of 100 to 150 meters in 1907, but he continued to build—and to break—machines with unique persistency. Captain Ferber was at work on a new biplane. Robert Esnault-Pelterie was continuing to develop his monoplane and had begun to design his engine. Trajan Vuia succeeded in making a few very short flights in his radically new monoplane.[5]

Slowly the flights increased in distance, in speed, and in controllability. Although these flights could not compare in any way with the previous achievements of the Wrights, nevertheless the activity in France was like the incoming tide, slowly creeping toward the goal, and made up of a number of individual efforts which swelled the total to a formidable array of competitors.

The Wrights were not yet concerned, as Chanute described their plans in a letter to Moedebeck written on March 2, shortly after a visit to Dayton:

They are negotiating [*sic*] with several parties, but they ask much too high a price in my judgment.

The Wrights say they are in no hurry to sell. That within five years a war is likely to break out in the world which will make a

---

[4] *The Aeronautical Journal* (London), Vol. XI (July, 1907), 49.

[5] Octave Chanute, "First Steps in Aviation and Memorable Flights," *Aeronautics* (New York), Vol. IV, No. 1 (January, 1909), 24; *Scientific American*, Vol. 96 (April 13, 1907), 315; Adams, *Flug*, 99; Lougheed, *Vehicles of the Air*, 157.

market for their invention, while none of their competitors are likely to catch up with them within five years.

Moedebeck did not, naturally, agree with this view, and replied to Chanute on March 20, "Concerning the Wright brothers nothing is now heard in Europe. They are forgotten."

Meanwhile the Wrights had begun their travels. In January they went to New York to discuss arrangements with Charles Flint, and returned home with several proposals under consideration but without a signed contract. Flint had written to Hart O. Berg, his associate in Europe, who became interested in the Wright patents and eventually was their principal promoter. Berg had many important and influential contacts with various governments of Europe, having been head of the Belgian National Gun Works which produced the Browning pistol and machine gun. Just a few years before he met the Wrights, Berg had promoted the sale of Simon Lake's submarine to the Russian Government.[6] His many interests included also automobiles, and at this time Berg built the first large auto factory in France and manufactured autos in the United States as well. Having become interested in the Wrights, Berg added aviation to his other interests.[7]

The brothers made another trip to New York in April, and again returned home without having reached an agreement. The visit had important results, however, for barely five weeks later Flint telegraphed that one of them was to sail immediately for Europe. On the very same evening Wilbur left Dayton for New York.

Katharine Wright has been described as having mortgaged the Wright home in order to finance this trip, but this was hardly possible on one day's notice. More important, Orville recently was quoted as denying this and the tales of her other

6 Bia, *Les Frères Wright et Leur Oeuvre,* 49.

7 *The New York Times,* December 10, 1941; Peyrey, *Les Oiseaux Artificiels,* 204.

financial contributions, in the following forthright statement issued through his secretary:

... the story that his sister Katherine gave financial and mathematical help was a very pretty one, but not true. She was her brothers' closest confidante and comrade, but it is a fable, without foundation, that she contributed to her brothers' success scientifically or financially.[8]

Wilbur sailed on the S.S. *Campania* for London. There he was met by Hart O. Berg, and after two days they proceeded to Paris at the end of May. Wilbur was fortunate in being taken around Europe by a man of Berg's experience and sophistication. On his side, Berg was immediately impressed by Wilbur's qualities: his integrity was instantly visible to Berg, who felt also, as he later remarked, that here was a man who had never lied.[9]

Negotiations with the French War Department consumed the next several months. While in Paris, Wilbur made his first balloon trip, and the rumor went the rounds that right after this trip he received—and refused—an offer from M. Deutsch of 300,000 francs. Deutsch was actually present at the conferences, along with Berg, and he was at this time trying to push along the negotiations with the French War Department. The outlook was so hopeful in July that Wilbur cabled Orville to come over immediately and to bring their dismantled planes. The French contract, so it seemed at this moment, was ready to be closed, and at better terms than had previously been offered.

Again, the promise of results was not fulfilled, and the Wrights withdrew their offer to the French.

Next they went to Berlin. Here, too, negotiations dragged, and the brothers returned to Paris. Once more they were involved in slow complicated maneuverings there.

[8] Charles E. Planck, *Women with Wings*, 40.
[9] Bia, *Les Frères Wright et Leur Oeuvre*, 6.

Captain Ferber, who had been so zealous in trying to forward the negotiations in France and who had tried several times to purchase a Wright plane, did not impress Wilbur. He believed that Ferber had changed his attitude and was now trying to hamper the negotiations. Chanute, agreeing with this view, replied on August 5:

I had surmised the facts about Captain Ferber to be as you state and I have no doubt that many of the people with whom you have to deal are intensely jealous of you. I trust, however, that you will overcome all difficulties in your way.

If there is anything on this side of the water that I can do, please command me.

Although both brothers were in Europe, Wilbur was featured in the accounts of the time. "Featured" is too strong a word, for he refused to grant interviews and kept out of all accounts whenever possible. The press was reduced to quoting his refusal to be interviewed in the following ungracious words: "I am here on business and pay no attention to the furor which is being made about me. I cannot talk at the moment."[10]

But Wilbur's rare smile and his notable brevity of speech were also noted in France. Georges Bia, later the Wright representative in Belgium, said defensively in a lecture about the Wrights:

I can assure you that Wilbur Wright, to speak only about him because I knew only Wilbur personally, knew how to arouse lively interest in his listeners, on those days when he felt inclined to conversation![11]

Published reports at this same time were sometimes less favorable, such as one in which Wilbur was quoted as saying, after he had observed the experiments at Issy of Henry Farman, *"C'est là un jeu d'enfant."*[12]

[10] *Almanach des Aviateurs pour 1909*, 20.
[11] Bia, *Les Frères Wright et Leur Oeuvre*, 3.
[12] *Almanach des Aviateurs pour 1909*, 20.

This was reported at the very time that Farman (English sportsman who had long resided in France) was making almost daily records for distance: on October 15 he beat Santos-Dumont's record by covering 918 feet (285 meters); on October 26, Farman flew 2,530 feet (771 meters) in his Voisin plane, the longest flight by far yet recorded in Europe, and also succeeded in sweeping a half-circle.[13]

Santos-Dumont had spent several months on experiments with a hydroplane, a new airship (#16), and several aeroplanes. Then he reverted again to monoplanes, and on November 17 appeared with his new airplane #19. This was the lightest and simplest machine yet produced, and it was reported that Santos-Dumont had turned it out in two weeks.[14]

The race was now between Santos-Dumont and Farman for the Deutsch-Archdeacon prize. Santos-Dumont made two attempts in November, but failed. Farman continued to show steady improvement in his flying, and, also in November, came close to winning the prize. He made a circle, but the flight was three feet short of the required distance.[15]

Noting this rapid progress, Chanute wrote to Wilbur on July 11: "Have you changed your opinion that you will not be caught up with for five years, now that you have seen what other aviators are doing?" And later, as the tempo of successes quickened, Chanute wrote again in December, "it may take less than the five years you estimated for one of them to catch up with you."

Chanute had put his finger on the point: The Wrights, seeing for the first time the French efforts, were finally con-

[13] *Scientific American*, Vol. 97 (November 9, 1907), 320; Chanute, "Chronology of Aviation," Smithsonian Institution, 1910 *Annual Report*, 163.

[14] Gondin da Foncesca, *Santos Dumont*, 65; Ferber, *L'Aviation*, 100 (German ed., 122); *Scientific American*, Vol. 96 (March 9, 1907), 213; (June 15, 1907), 490; Vol. 97 (December 14, 1907), 445; Vol. 98 (January 11, 1908), 26.

[15] *Scientific American*, Vol. 97 (November 23, 1907), 378; (December 14, 1907), 445.

cerned by their apparent success. But they were not, as was Chanute, fearful of real competition from the French, for they were more than ever convinced of the superiority of their own plane. What worried the Wrights was a subtler fact: The expectations aroused by the French successes were as harmful to the Wrights' negotiations as though these competitors were in actual possession of machines equal to theirs. The psychological effect on their business was what they feared, not the possibility that their own plane might be inferior.

With their usual sagacity, the Wrights had not only kept their fences in order throughout this year, but they had actually improved them. Their new engine gave 50 per cent more power than the 1905 engine; its power was sufficient to carry two men, plus fuel, plus an extra load of one hundred pounds. When Wilbur went to Europe, Orville had put together a new machine designed to carry two men. The position of the operators was changed so that both men could sit side by side, and thus either man, or both together, could control the plane.

This was farsighted planning, for it meant that they were prepared to teach others to fly as soon as they had concluded a contract. They estimated that they could teach an intelligent man to handle the plane in not over a week's time—a contrast to the many years of effort it had taken them to learn to fly.

In the meantime, they labored under the disadvantage of having made no flights at all since 1905, whereas other men were flying constantly. But the Wrights always had the inestimable advantage of knowing exactly what they wanted, and their tenacity in continuing on their chosen road more often than not made up for such temporary disadvantages. They continued to refuse, therefore, to fly their plane in public; they would not compete for the many prizes, amounting to several hundreds of thousands of dollars, all of which they could easily have won; they would not publish descriptions of their planes. But they continued to prepare with foresight and care for the time when they had sold their plane to some government.

The world knew nothing of these activities, and was only vaguely aware of the fact that Wilbur had returned home without any foreign commitments, leaving Orville in Paris. In spite of continued rumors about them in the press, attention focused on the French flyers, particularly Santos-Dumont, Farman, and Bleriot. In this country, also, there were some promising experiments, among them the brilliant glides executed by Lawrence J. Lesh, a fifteen-year-old boy whom Chanute was financing. The latest plane of Israel Ludlow—a large machine mounted on pontoons—was being tried out.[16]

Important work was being carried on in Nova Scotia, where Glenn H. Curtiss had spent the summer with Bell building a motor for Bell's tetrahedral kite. The kite was tested late this year, under the direction of Lieutenant Selfridge. The results were so encouraging, and the group (which in the meantime included also two young Canadian engineers, F. W. Baldwin and J. A. D. McCurdy) so enthusiastic, that Mrs. Bell suggested the formation of an association for the purpose of building a powered plane. Hopes ran high for the scientific results which the new Aerial Experiment Association would produce.[17]

To outsiders and to those interested in the Wrights alike, the work being carried on all over the world seemed to complete the eclipse of the brothers. It was all very well for them to toss off a paragraph on the possibility of flying five hundred miles, but other men were actually making flights which, even though they might be measured only in feet and yards, could be seen. The Wrights were running a race against time, and it seemed that they were losing it.

Even Chanute, continuing his interest although he re-

[16] *Scientific American*, Vol. 97 (September 14, 1907), 190; (October 19, 1907), 272.

[17] Elsbeth E. Freudenthal, *The Aviation Business*, 9.

ceived few letters from Wilbur on this first trip to Europe, believed that the brothers would win or lose according to what would be achieved in the following few months. Soon after Wilbur had gone to Europe Chanute wrote to Orville about an article he had been writing on European developments in aviation:

I think that Wilbur's views will be modified by his journey. ... The result [of Chanute's studies for his article] has been to convince me that the Europeans are catching up with you more rapidly than I had believed. Of course they will meet many mishaps and breakages, but they are learning from each failure, especially as the various aviators are present at each other's trials and are educating each other.

Chanute's opinion had not changed by December, although he did not emphasize it in the following tactful letter to Wilbur:

I am very glad to receive your letter of 9th, giving an account of your negociations in France and in Germany. I am about to file it with your other letters and it may be that in a score of years it will prove of historical interest.

I regret that you have not made more positive sales. It looks to me as if the Government officials are keeping you dangling in the expectation that some of your competitors will discover the secret and they can get your invention cheaper. ...

My feeling would be to sell, even though you do not get your original price, which I always thought too high. ...

How did Orville manage to get Malaria, in Paris of all places. I supposed that French cooking was building him up, although not to the extent shown in the enclosed picture, in which I hardly recognized him. ...

P. S. I have taken the liberty of having the Geographic Magazine sent to you for one year.

The Wrights were all but forgotten, and Chanute was deeply concerned. At this moment, when they needed it most, the United States Government came to their rescue—and startled the aeronautical world.[18] The Board of Ordnance and Fortifications of the War Department announced on December 23, 1907, that it would award contracts for one airship and one heavier-than-air craft. This was the same board which had granted $50,000 for Langley's experiments, and which had refused funds for another trial of Langley's aerodrome.

The announcement was invaluable to the brothers. They had tried for two years to obtain a contract with some European government. They had written letters and then had walked government corridors, without success. They had met skepticism of their ability to deliver a plane, and doubt of the value of their patents. The hesitation of other governments had been increased by the fact that the Wrights' own country had not given them a contract.

Now the United States took the lead over the rest of the world in announcing a competition for an aeroplane. The conditions of this competition at first astounded the aeronautical world, for they seemed, as European and American journals complained, to assume that "flying machines are almost a usual method of transportation."[19] The conditions, in short, seemed so difficult as to be impossible. James Means wrote to Chanute, "Do you suppose that they intentionally asked for impossible things, or didn't they know any better?"

It was gradually realized that the specifications were intended to be met by only one plane, the Wright brothers' "Flyer." As Chanute implied when he answered Means's letter, "It does not ask for impossible things, but there is but one machine in existence which can comply with the conditions."

As a matter of fact, Wilbur had been in conference with General James Allen of the War Department early in December. Wilbur believed that public bids were asked for to avoid public criticism of the board's action, and also to try out

<hr />

[18] George O. Squier, "The Wright Brothers—A Bit of History," *Flight* (London), Vol. V (June 14, 1913), 651.

the opinion of the country. Actually he had informed the War Department of their asking price, and this sum had been earmarked before the advertisement was issued.[20]

Lieutenant Colonel George O. Squier, on giving the first Wilbur Wright Memorial Lecture in England several years later, stated that "the Wright Brothers came to the War Department, and informed us what they could do, and they so convinced the authorities that the money was found to give them their first contract."[21] These facts were not, of course, generally known when the War Department published its announcement.

Considering the elementary stage of the art, the provisions of the competition seemed too stiff to meet: The army required that the machine carry two men and sufficient fuel for a flight of 125 miles; minimum speed was set at thirty-six miles per hour; bonuses were offered for speeds over forty miles per hour. The machine had to stay in the air for at least one hour and had to land without any serious damage. A particularly difficult requirement was that, during this trial flight of one hour, the machine "must be steered in all directions without difficulty and at all times under perfect control and equilibrium."

In spite of the advances in the art since that time, the advertisement contained provisions which even modern manufacturers would not like to have to meet: The machine "should be so designed as to ascend in any country which may be encountered in field service. . . . It should also land in a field without requiring a specially prepared spot and without damaging its structure." Another provision required that the plane be assembled and put into operating condition in about

[19] Chanute, "Recent Aeronautical Progress in the United States," *The Aeronautical Journal* (London), Vol. XII, No. 47 (July, 1908), 52.

[20] Kelly, *The Wright Brothers*, 208.

[21] Squier, "The Wright Brothers—A Bit of History," *Flight* (London), Vol. V (June 14, 1913), 651–52.

one hour, and that it should be quickly "taken apart and packed for transportation in army wagons."[22]

The specifications were indeed hard, but, as Chanute wrote about this advertisement:

The Signal Service officers answer that the specifications were drawn up after interviews with some of the inventors and merely cover what they said they could perform, while some clauses were added to prevent the Government's being trifled with, and that the tests will be conducted with judicious reason and liberality. More especially does this apply to the granting of 3 trials each for the speed test and the endurance test of 1 hour.[23]

The picture had brightened considerably for the Wrights. Wilbur had at least influenced the terms of this announcement which, while containing severe conditions, could easily be met by the brothers' plane. Hart O. Berg was making back-stage arrangements for a contract in France. Orville, also in France, was keeping in touch with developments there, and, in spite of malaria, was having several engines built.

The business of manufacturing planes was just beginning in France, where the Voisin brothers had already built planes for Farman and Delagrange, and where Levavasseur had turned out his famous Antoinette motor, used by Santos-Dumont and Bleriot.[24]

The Wrights were preparing to challenge this market: they planned to build about six new planes for the European spring season. This was a heavy program, but the brothers, thirty-six and forty years old, had sufficient energy to plan and to carry out all the details involved in this bi-continental activity.

[22] Squier, "The Present Status of Military Aeronautics," *Journal* of the American Society of Mechanical Engineers, Vol. XXX (December, 1908), Appendix 1.

[23] Chanute, "Recent Aeronautical Progress in the United States," *The Aeronautical Journal* (London), Vol. XII, No. 47 (July, 1908), 53–54.

[24] Adams, *Flug*, 97, 98, 100.

CHAPTER XI

From Kitty Hawk to Paris–1908

EVERYTHING COMBINED in 1908 to bring these quiet, retiring men into the blaze of world-wide fame. The exciting events of the first half-year were a crescendo for the climaxes of the second half, when, beginning in August, Wilbur in France and Orville in the United States held the world's attention by their exploits. The brothers' characteristics, which little fitted them for the role of heroes, for a brief period were capitalized successfully, and for a short time helped, as is usual in the upswing toward widespread popularity, to endear them to the public.

During the first half of 1908 attention continued to focus on the great activity in flying displayed in France. The art seemed to have been almost neglected in this country in comparison with the many experiments being carried out at Issy and other flying fields. Although the work of Bell's Aerial Experiment Association offered a gleam of hope here, the United States seemed to have lost its chance of taking a foremost place in aeronautics. The best talent in this country—the Wright brothers—continued to shun the limelight and to concentrate on their own private business. They continued to refuse to make a public flight and to avoid reporters and interviews whenever possible. Their mysteriousness and silence increased the resentment caused by unfulfilled curiosity.

When, on January 13, Henry Farman won the Deutsch-Archdeacon prize of 50,000 francs ($10,000) for flying over one kilometer in a closed circle, he was hailed as the hero of the hour.[1] The sculptor Delagrange then made the first flight

[1] Adams, *Flug*, 99; *Scientific American*, Vol. 98 (January 25, 1908), 54.

with a passenger in history; gracefully, his passenger was Henry Farman.[2] A short time later, on April 11, Delagrange beat Farman's record by flying a distance of two and one-half miles in six minutes, thirty seconds.[3]

Captain Ferber's long years of effort were rewarded when the Antoinette Company, with which he was associated, built his #9 plane. Ferber demonstrated this in a successful flight in this year, and remarked wryly that it showed what his #8 (of which the #9 was a copy) could have achieved in 1905.[4] Bleriot continued to experiment and to build planes. His persistent efforts continued in spite of accidents and delays, causing Chanute to describe him as the man who "has built and broken more machines than any other aviator in the world." In July, Bleriot made a flight of over eight minutes.[5]

The first public demonstration of a successful flight by a heavier-than-air machine in the United States occurred on March 9, 1908. This was five years after the Wrights' flights at Kitty Hawk, which we now consider the first flights. But the same difference that existed between Santos-Dumont's flights of 1906 and the Wrights' 1903 flights now existed between this flight in March, 1908, and the Wrights' first flights. Therefore, when the *Red Wing* of the Aerial Experiment Association flew 319 feet on March 9, it was hailed as the first public flight in this country, and Chanute wrote about it in an article at this time, "this being the first public exhibition of the flight of a heavier than air machine in America."[6]

The *Red Wing,* designed largely by Lieutenant Selfridge, took off from frozen Lake Keuka, near Curtiss' factory at Hammondsport, New York. After flying 319 feet, it was dam-

[2] *Scientific American,* Vol. 98 (April 11, 1908), 256.

[3] Chanute, "Chronology of Aviation," Smithsonian Institution, 1910 *Annual Report,* 161; *Almanach des Aviateurs pour 1909,* 14.

[4] Ferber, *L'Aviation,* 82 (German ed., 103).

[5] Chanute, "Recent Progress in Aviation," Smithsonian Institution, 1910 *Annual Report,* 153.

[6] Chanute, "Recent Aeronautical Progress in the United States," *The Aeronautical Journal* (London), Vol. XII, No. 47 (July, 1908), 53.

aged on landing.[7] While this was an important event, the
flight did not compare with the achievements at this same time
of the French flyers. Nor did the distance of 319 feet augur
well for an early fulfillment of the United States War Department's requirement of a flight of over one hour.

The first pride in the War Department's advertisement for
a flying machine had given way to great skepticism of the
ability to fulfill its difficult terms, and James Means in January
had again written to Chanute about the terms:

> I think that if the War Department really wanted a "heavier-
> than-air" flying machine they would save a lot of time if they made
> most of the conditions easier than they have.
>
> I believe that Minerva came forth, full fledged, from the fore-
> head of Jupiter, but I hardly think that the perfect flying-machine
> will appear in such sudden fashion.

When the bids for the competition were opened in February, it was found that forty-one had been submitted, a large
number, indicating the interest in aeronautics here. Only three
were able to qualify for the competition: the Wright brothers,
Augustus M. Herring, and J. F. Scott of Chicago. Finally
Scott withdrew, and only the bid of Herring (for $20,000),
and that of the Wrights (for $25,000) remained. Delivery of
the Herring plane was to be made in 180 days; that of the
Wrights in 200 days, or by August 27, with another thirty
days allowed for passing the tests.

Thus the field narrowed down to the Wrights and Herring,
whose reappearance on the aeronautics scene was not a cause
for surprise. Chanute, who had known Herring since he had
first engaged him to work in 1896 and who regretted having
taken Herring with him to Kitty Hawk in 1902, nevertheless
appreciated Herring's lifelong devotion to aeronautics, and
wished him success in this competition. Always aware that
there must be more than one successful solution of the prob-

[7] Zahm, *Aerial Navigation*, 265.

lems of flying, Chanute was eager that Herring, as well as the Wrights, reap rewards for his years of work.[8] Chanute knew, from Wilbur's few remarks about the competition, that they had a certain advantage over Herring, for he wrote to Means, "I suspect, however, that they [Wright brothers] have some sort of an inside arrangement at Washington which will be much to their benefit."

On the other hand, the brothers' long memories cherished a mistrust of Herring (shared by Chanute), which had not been decreased by his almost threatening letter early in 1904 suggesting that their patents might overlap and, prophetically, might someday be the basis for long and expensive lawsuits. But they were too busy at this time to bother about the news which Chanute had relayed in December about Herring:

Captain Hildebrandt told me when here that he had been told by Herring in New York that he (Herring) knew your secret, having had it unconscionably divulged by two eye witnesses who had described the machine as it appeared in the air. What that secret was Herring did not say.

It did not pass unnoticed that the Wrights' bid of $25,000 in this competition was far below their offer to sell to the French Government in 1905 for 1,000,000 francs ($200,000). It was indeed a great reduction from the $100,000 price they had asked of the United States government only a year before. Their low bid may have been due to the fact that delivery of their plane to the United States Government did not include delivery of their patents, which were, they insisted, their chief assets. On the other hand, it meant that they were willing to take the risk, which they had always avoided, of having their plane copied after it was flown in public, and of becoming involved in patent litigation.

The Wrights were thus able to change their plans to meet

---

[8] Chanute, "Recent Aeronautical Progress in the United States," *The Aeronautical Journal* (London), Vol. XII, No. 47 (July, 1908), 54–55.

changing conditions. While they believed themselves still to be far in advance of other competitors, they had had to meet the handicapping belief that they would soon be surpassed. The facts bore out their convictions: the others had not yet caught up with the brothers, who were still secure in their business arrangements, patents, and superior skill.

Chanute obviously did not agree with this point of view and wrote to Wilbur on January 4, 1908:

I am glad to infer, from your letter of the 1st, that you consider the net advance of your competitors to be less threatening to your interests than I had feared, and that the condition of your own negociations is satisfactory to you.

In spite of their feeling of security, the Wrights were being increasingly hard pressed by the successes of other flyers. The competition of the French advances in the art could not much longer be ignored. Already in January, Farman's record flight had been the cause of various editorials, such as one in the *New York Herald* which said that Farman had placed the Wright brothers "in a position where they must either demonstrate the superiority of their invention or yield the honors to Mr. Farman."[9]

Twice in this year Farman specifically challenged the Wrights to fly in open competition with him. The brothers replied to these challenges in their usual oblique way. Their answer was to enter the government competition, which called for exploits that no one, including Farman, had remotely approached in public flight.

Their immediate problem was to get into flying practice again, since they had not flown at all since October, 1905. After an absence of five years, they returned in May, 1908, to their old camp at Kill Devil, and found their buildings showing the effects of the elements during their long absence.

[9] *New York Herald*, January 14, 1908.

"After tedious delays in repairing our old camp," as they wrote,[10] they were able to get sufficient order out of the wreckage so that they were ready to begin to fly again.

Their privacy at Kitty Hawk was forever lost. Reporters flocked down to this isolated spot to see the brothers fly—and came up against the stone wall of the Wrights' determination not yet to be seen and not to give out interviews.

The Wrights' mistrust of journalists, always great, had been increased by George Kibbe Turner's article in the February *McClure's Magazine,* which had aroused Wilbur to strong anger. Turner had not, Wilbur felt, given direct quotations of what they had said, but had rehashed their old articles and had pretended that they were quotations. As was their policy, they did nothing to correct the tinge of inaccuracy to which they objected, in spite of Chanute's urgings: "I believe that you do not do full justice to Mr. Turner for the McClure article. He wrote me that he had endeavored to be as exact as possible and to add nothing of his own to what you actually said. If he has misrepresented you, why do you not write to him?"[11]

Whatever the scientific inaccuracies of his article, Turner's personal impressions of the Wrights give us an excellent picture:

> Orville, of the more social and conversational temperament, did the greater share of the talking—an amiable, kindly-faced man of thirty-five. Wilbur—prematurely bald, about forty, with the watchful eyes, marked facial lines, and dry, brief speech of a naturally reticent man—corroborated or amplified his brother's statements.

Turner was impressed by the "two lean, quiet men in a dingy, commonplace, little brick bicycle-shop," and by their per-

10 Wright, "Our Aeroplane Tests at Kitty Hawk," *Scientific American,* Vol. 98 (June 13, 1908), 423.

11 Only in 1910, when Turner's article was introduced as evidence in the lawsuits, did Wilbur state his opinion of it publicly, saying that it contained "many statements which were not correct." U. S. Circuit Court of Appeals, 2nd circuit, Wright Co. *vs.* Louis Paulhan, 283.

Wilbur Wright at Hunadières, France, in 1908

Orville Wright at Fort Myer, September 12, 1908

Count de Lambert chats with Orville Wright
after his airplane flight over Paris, 1909

sonalities, which were "pleasant, but unassuming, most approachable." He noted also that they were "shy and silent."[12]

Having these characteristics, the brothers were naturally not inclined to welcome the reporters who flocked to Kitty Hawk. The reporters hid behind sand dunes, in spite of vicious attacks of the mosquitoes, and, using their spyglasses, sent out news through the Weather Bureau telegraph at Manteo.[13] So doubting was the outside world that one reporter (D. Bruce Salley) received a telegram from his editor cautioning him not to send any more "wild-cat stuff."

Chanute described the brothers-*versus*-press impasse in an article in the *Aeronautical Journal* (London):

The spot is very secluded, but the ubiquitous reporter has found the camp and is sending "news," both true and untrue, to the great annoyance of Wright Brothers, from Manteo, a little town on Roanoke Island, the seat of Sir Walter Raleigh's first settlement in 1585. This is about six miles from the camp.

An amusing struggle has resulted. The reporters are frantic for information, and the Wrights most determined that no description be given of their apparatus.[14]

Their actual flying practice was exceedingly short, but they accomplished at least thirteen flights in the days from May 6 to May 14, and made many circles. The plane was the same one they had flown in 1905, but they had altered it somewhat in order to meet the government requirements. They wrote: "The operator assumed a sitting position, instead of lying prone, as in 1905, and a seat was added for a passenger. A larger motor was installed, and radiators and gasolene [*sic*] reservoirs of larger capacity replaced those previously used."[15]

12 George Kibbe Turner, "The Men Who Learned to Fly," *McClure's Magazine,* Vol. XXX, No. 4 (February, 1908), 444.

13 *Scientific American,* Vol. 98 (May 23, 1908), 367.

14 Chanute, "Recent Aeronautical Progress in the United States," *The Aeronautical Journal* (London), Vol. XII, No. 47 (July, 1908), 54–55.

15 Wright, "The Wright Brothers' Aeroplane," *Century Magazine,* Vol. LXXVI, No. 5 (September, 1908), 650.

Their flights being for the purpose of becoming familiar with the alterations, they made no attempts to achieve distances or altitude. On May 14 they took up a passenger for the first time, and covered two and one-half miles in three minutes, forty seconds. Their last and longest flight on this date ended in an accident, which stopped their practice. Although, as they wrote, giving an excellent example of their rigorous adherence to schedules: "Repairs could have been made in a week's time, but the time allowed for these experiments having elapsed, we were compelled to close experiments for the present."[16]

That the brothers were pleased with their eight days of flying was shown by the closing paragraph of their article, published in the *Scientific American* the following month:

The machine showed a speed of nearly 41 miles an hour with two men on board, and a little over 44 miles with one man. The control was very satisfactory in winds of 15 to 20 miles an hour, and there was no distinguishable difference in control when traveling with, against, or across the wind.[17]

After their machine crashed, the brothers returned to Dayton to prepare for another separation from each other. While Orville stayed at home to prepare the plane for the United States Government tests in August, Wilbur was to go to France to fulfill the terms of their contract with a French syndicate.

After four years of bargaining and fruitless negotiations, the Wrights had finally signed a contract. It was not with a government, as they had always hoped, but with a French commercial group promoted by Hart O. Berg and headed by Lazare Weiller. The contract provided that the brothers were to make two flights of fifty kilometers (thirty-one miles) each,

[16] Wright, "Our Aeroplane Tests at Kitty Hawk," *Scientific American,* Vol. 98 (June 13, 1908), 423.
[17] *Ibid.*

within a week, and with a passenger; and that they were then to teach three men to fly their plane.[18] These provisions did not unduly disturb the brothers, for they believed that flying could be taught in a week's time and that flying was, in fact, no harder than learning to ride a bicycle.[19]

The terms of the contract were good: the brothers were to receive 500,000 francs ($100,000) in cash, and one-half the founders' shares, which were entitled to 50 per cent of the profits after interest. The contract included commercial and government rights to their French patents for France and her colonies. Four machines, besides the one used in their demonstration flights, were to be sold to the syndicate at 20,000 francs ($4,000) each, or a total of 80,000 francs ($16,000), of which Wilbur estimated that about one-half would be profit.

Again the Wrights had reduced their price; they had come down from the $25,000 bid to the United States to $4,000 per plane to their French company. This decrease was partially due to competition, which began this early in the history of the aeroplane. There were already several aeroplane factories near Paris, of which at least one—that of the famous Voisin brothers, who built Farman's and Delagrange's planes—could turn out four machines a month, and at a price of $4,000. The price in the United States for a Farman-Delagrange plane was reported to be $9,000. Here, too, competition was beginning, for Bell's Aerial Experiment Association was offering, in June, to build a plane, deliverable within sixty days, for $5,000.[20]

The offer by the Association showed the success it had achieved in a brief six months. Its second plane, the *White Wing*, was flown in May for a distance of 1,017 feet. Designed

[18] Bia, *Les Frères Wright et Leur Oeuvre,* 54; Adams, *Flug,* 88; Zahm, *Aerial Navigation,* 271; *Scientific American,* Vol. 99 (August 1, 1908), 75; (October 17, 1908), 258.

[19] *Automotor Journal* (London), Vol. XIII, No. 34 (August 22, 1908), 1122.

[20] *Scientific American,* Vol. 98 (April 11, 1908), 256; (June 6, 1908), 407; Vol. 99 (November 21, 1908), 356, 358.

largely by F. W. Baldwin, it was piloted by Curtiss, who then supervised the construction of the Association's third plane. By June, this plane, appropriately called the *June Bug,* was ready to try. It was so successful that Curtiss decided to make an attempt to win the Scientific American trophy (announced in 1907).[21]

On July 4, 1908, in the presence of officials from the Aero Club of America, Curtiss flew the *June Bug* a distance of more than one kilometer. In addition to winning the trophy, this important flight indicated the excellent results already attained by the Association, and augured Curtiss's future importance in the field.

However, the Wrights believed and later claimed that these excellent results had been achieved because the planes were designed after theirs, including the adjustable wing tips. This was the crux of their later lawsuit against Curtiss. Wilbur wrote a letter in 1910 to the *Scientific American,* saying that soon after Bell had formed the Aerial Experiment Association, the secretary, Lieutenant Selfridge, had written a letter which Wilbur described as follows:

Lieut. Selfridge wrote to the brothers Wright in behalf of the association, asking for information regarding the construction of gliders, and was referred to the drawings and description in the Wright American patent and the drawings and description in the Aerophile article of 1903. Lieut. Selfridge in answer said he had obtained a copy of the patent, and hoped to obtain the other paper soon. At first only the general form of the Wright machine was copied in the machines constructed by Mr. Curtiss, but soon the adjustable tips began to appear, their necessity having become apparent. It was only in 1908 that Mr. Curtiss began using adjustable tips.[22]

Immediately after Curtiss's flight on July 4, Orville wrote

---

[21] Zahm, *Aerial Navigation,* 266.

[22] W. Wright, "The Earliest Wright Flights—A Letter from Wilbur Wright," *Scientific American,* Vol. 103 (July 16, 1910), 47.

him that the *June Bug* infringed their patent No. 821,393. He added that they could not, themselves, do exhibition flying because "the commercial part of our business is taking up so much of our time," but that they would be glad to consider the matter of a license if Curtiss intended to enter the exhibition field. Curtiss replied that he did not expect to do so and was flying for scientific purposes as a member of the Aerial Experiment Association; that he had referred the patent matter to the secretary of the Association.[23]

Curtiss continued to work with the Association for a brief period. The Wrights quietly prepared to fulfill their French contract and to prepare for the American competition. The excitement about Curtiss's July flight subsided, and interest soon shifted from Hammondsport to Le Mans, scene of the first public demonstration of flying by one of the mysterious Wright brothers.

Wilbur arrived in France in July and made preparations to fly at the race track at Hunaudières, near Le Mans. The French press received him with skepticism and open hostility, as he calmly and slowly prepared his machine for a flight. Nothing would hurry him, it seemed, and his caution was attributed to fear, cowardice, and other qualities that were highly undesirable. He was, it seemed, a typical example of the too-well-known "American bluff."

An English magazine described the situation with some amusement: "He comes to France enveloped in a cloud of rumor . . . . leisurely selects a suitable spot, and thereafter settles himself down on it with such quiet serenity as to be a perpetual irritation to the typically French temperament."[24]

A French journalist remarked, *"Lorqu'il arriva en France, Wilbur Wright était non seulement flegmatique, mais fa-*

23 U. S. Circuit Court, Western District of New York, I, 52–53 (Orville Wright on July 20, 1908; Curtiss on July 24, 1908.)

24 *Automotor Journal* (London), Vol. XIII, No. 37 (September 12, 1908), 1208.

rouche." He attributed this mood to Wilbur's disappointment about the previous fruitless negotiations and to the stories concocted about the brothers in the American press.[25]

Wilbur continued to work on his machine in his quiet, unassuming way, apparently untouched by the fact that his delay in flying was the subject of popular songs and jokes. But, a sensitive man always, he felt the hostility and skepticism of the French—which he was facing alone and without Orville. One rhyme, popular at this time in France, follows:

> *C'est dificile de voir vole Orville*
> *C'est bien plus dur de voir voler Wilbur.*[26]

Some few men continued to believe in him, largely because of Chanute's backing, and a British journal reproved the French for their doubts in the following editorial, which included also a slight dig at the Wrights:

The sudden discovery of the Wright Brothers and their machine *in France* by some of our contemporaries would be amusing if it did not foster the disbelief which is borne of ignorance. Mr. Wright deserves better than that, even if he has defied the Press and evinced a shocking intolerance of the ubiquitous snapshotter. After all, the Wrights are perfectly entitled to behave as seems proper to them with a view to maintaining the market value of their research, and although, from what appears on the surface, it would seem as if they may have been a little too ambitous in the matter of trying to realize a fortune, no one has a right to judge them harshly—or to disparage their *bona fides*—on that account.[27]

In the meantime, Henry Farman had come to the United States in August under a contract to give exhibition flights at Brighton Beach. But the race track was too small to turn at high speed, and the flights were therefore all straightaway. After ten days, the gate receipts, never large, had fallen off

[25] Peyrey, *Les Oiseaux Artificiels,* 202.
[26] *Automotor Journal* (London), Vol. XIII (September 5, 1908), 1185.
[27] *Ibid.,* Vol. XIII, No. 34 (August 22, 1908), 1121.

entirely, and Farman stopped flying. His visit was a failure. After only a few weeks here, Farman left abruptly for France, disappointed that even on the first day of his public flights there had been only a few thousand spectators.[28] The distance from New York to Brighton Beach was then great, but a more important factor in Farman's failure to attract crowds was the fact that actually the American people were not yet aware of the advent of flying. Soon their interest would be stirred deeply.

One day in August, 1908, Wilbur Wright calmly took off from the field near Le Mans, and flew! Although his first flight on August 8 lasted only one minute and forty-five seconds, Wilbur circled the field and showed a control of his machine far beyond anything ever seen before.[29] He continued to make several flights a day and increased his times and distances, so that five days after his first flight, he circled the field seven times. And then, finding Hunaudières too small, he moved to a larger field.[30]

The work of other men now seemed to have been merely the preliminaries for Wilbur's more brilliant flights. It was as though a stage manager had placed the others first on a program as curtain raisers, with their struggles to achieve flights of fifty feet, one thousand feet, and then a few thousand feet. The next-best talent had then "come on"—the men who painfully tried to turn circles and flew a few miles. These prior efforts had aroused the enthusiasm of the public and had, as well, educated them in the difficulties of flying.

Now the public and aeronauts alike were ready to understand and appreciate the mastery of flying that Wilbur displayed when he flew many miles, not feet, and turned his

[28] Jacques Sahel, *Henry Farman et l'Aviation,* 135, 137, 145; *Scientific American,* Vol. 99 (August 1, 1908), 75; (August 8, 1908), 86; (November 21, 1908), 350.

[29] *Westminster Gazette* (London), May 4, 1910, 11; Bia, *Les Frères Wright et Leur Oeuvre,* 28.

[30] *Scientific American,* Vol. 99 (August 22, 1908), 124; *Ibid.* (August 29, 1908), 135.

plane in perfect circles with as great ease as when he flew in a straight line. His control was, as he and Orville had written in the previous June, equally good "when traveling with, against, or across the wind."[31]

The grounds at Auvours were as crowded with spectators as had been Le Mans. To see Wilbur Wright fly became the fashion, and people came from all over the continent and England to his flying field. Royalty and *hoi polloi*, aeronauts and scientists, as well as capitalists and promoters, all crowded into automobiles, carriages, and trains, and streamed out to Auvours.

The great man continued to live simply, trying to do his own cooking—in France, of all places. He lived on the field, and practically slept with his machine, as described by his English admirer and biographer, Griffith Brewer:

A piece of stout canvas nailed between two pieces of 2 in. by 3 in. wood supported at their ends on the rafters of the shed containing the machine, formed the bed on which he slept. . . . The same shed, which by the by was too small to take the machine until the rudder had been folded back, served as his office as well as his bedroom.[32]

Another visitor was impressed by the lack of a kitchen, which was only "the corner where the heater served as a kitchen."[33] Wilbur got up early in the morning, usually at five o'clock, and consistently retired early at night, even leaving banquets given in his honor in order to get to bed.

The American public, which had been indifferent to the point of apathy about flying, and almost as indifferent to the existence of the Wright brothers, found its national pride

---

[31] Wright, "Our Aeroplane Tests at Kitty Hawk," *Scientific American*, Vol. 98 (June 13, 1908), 423.

[32] Brewer, "The Life and Work of Wilbur Wright," *The Aeronautical Journal* (London) Vol. XX, No. 79 (July–September, 1916), 129.

[33] Bia, *Les Frères Wright et Leur Oeuvre*, 7.

awakened by Wilbur's flights, and the more chauvinistic made this an excuse to start the eagle screaming. The French, also chauvinistic, nevertheless went out of their way to accord honors and glory to Wilbur. He appreciated this volte-face, and realized that the French people were now trying to make up for their former hostility.

This lesson in the variability of people's sentiments was not lost on Wilbur, but the Wrights were never in danger of succumbing to momentary adulation. Their poise was made more remarkable by the fact of their long years of previous work—and of waiting for just this moment. As throughout his life, Wilbur's interest was in his work, and his energies and thoughts were focused on his plane.

The French aviators, hitherto leaders of the world, were eclipsed. Leon Delagrange witnessed Wilbur's preliminary flights early in August and on seeing his "skilful figures of eight and other manoeuvres," is reported to have exclaimed, *"Eh bien. Nous n'existons pas. Nous sommes battus."*[34] Henry Farman was equally enthusiastic but felt dubious about Wilbur, remarking, "His apparatus is admirable from all points of view. But he is not sure of himself, nor of his machine."[35]

The general enthusiasm for Wilbur's exploits was reflected in the stimulation they gave to the French. They, too, made great advances in their flying, which were climaxed on September 6 when Delagrange made a flight of over fifteen miles in a little under thirty minutes. This was a world record. In a brief time Delagrange's record was surpassed—in the United States.

Early in September, Orville had gone to Fort Myer, Virginia, to deliver his plane for the United States Government tests. Like Wilbur, Orville made slow and careful preparations before flying, and several times postponed his initial flight. On September 9 word went around that Orville was

[34] *Automotor Journal* (London), August 15, 1908, 1087.
[35] Sahel, *Henry Farman et L'Aviation,* 172.

finally going to fly—and once more the American press muffed the ball.

The newsmen, oppressed by the heat, were too disgusted by their previous disappointments to come out to the field again. However, Augustus Post, the secretary of the Aero Club of America and enthusiastic promoter of its annual shows, went along with Orville on this hot day to the hangar. Post told of this day with great pleasure, for he and Orville were the only ones at the field.

Orville presently took off, and Post, purely to satisfy his own curiosity, looked at his watch. To Post's enormous surprise, Orville kept on flying, and Post kept his eyes glued to his watch, aware that he was the only witness. Orville flew a world's record of fifty-seven minutes, thirty-one seconds, by the clocking of his first homologator.

When they heard the news, the press streamed out to the field and saw Orville fly again on the same day, raising his own record to one hour, two and one-fourth minutes. A little later on the same afternoon Orville took up a passenger. This was Lieutenant Frank P. Lahm, son of Frank S. Lahm who had sent his cousin, Harvey Weaver, to visit the Wrights in 1905. The senior Lahm's interest in aeronautics not only started his son on his brilliant career, but also aroused the interest of his cousin, Ralph H. Upson, in aeronautics.[36]

On September 9, Orville, with Lahm as his passenger, flew six minutes, twenty-six seconds. By September 12, Orville, flying alone, achieved a flight lasting one hour, fifteen minutes—another record.

The world was thrilled by the friendly competition between Orville in the United States and Wilbur at Auvours.

---

[36] At Lahm's invitation Upson was present for these exciting tests in 1908; he later became a famous balloonist and was associated for many years with the Goodyear Company.

Major General Frank P. Lahm was retired from active duty in 1941 on reaching the statutory age limit of sixty-four, after an active and uniquely brilliant career in military aviation.

When Orville set a record, Wilbur was reported to be more gratified than anyone else, "although never a sign of surprise or exuberant display of joy was evinced by this sphinx-like aeronaut. It was just a case of what was naturally to be expected, with better to follow."[37]

And better did follow, for Wilbur topped Orville's record of one hour, fifteen minutes, by flying one hour, thirty-one minutes. Since there was never, and never could be, the slightest doubt of the brothers' extreme affection for each other, this fraternal display on two continents contained all the beguiling elements of a Horatio Alger story plus a fairy tale come to life.

What had previously been called the brothers' overcautiousness, and even bluffing, now was seen to be great care, compounded with brilliant skill, and based on sureness. This quiet self-confidence and sureness were the Wrights' chief assets and greatest contributions to aviation. They raised the problem of flight from the status of a fool's or a madman's dream, to which it had been for centuries relegated, to that of a practical means of locomotion. Masters of their planes, supreme in the world, Wilbur and Orville Wright were actually the first successful pilots in the history of flying.

At this moment of universal triumph, Orville met with a tragic accident. While flying on September 17 with Lieutenant Thomas E. Selfridge as his passenger, Orville's plane crashed to the ground. Selfridge was killed; Orville was seriously injured, and did not recover consciousness for several days.

Selfridge's death constituted a great loss to the art of aeronautics; he had made important contributions in his work with the Aerial Experiment Association. His heroic behavior during the few seconds of this crash was touchingly described by Orville to Heinrich Adams, a German admirer of the Wrights:

[37] *Automotor Journal* (London), September 19, 1908, 1247.

... in that brief time a wave of thoughts flooded his [Orville's] mind, but nevertheless he remembered clearly how his companion never once cried out. As the unusual noise started, Selfridge only looked questioningly at him.[38]

Chanute was the first to go to Orville's bedside. Katharine Wright left her high-school class in Dayton and stayed at the hospital until Orville was pronounced out of danger.

It was a great tragedy that this first fatality in a powered plane should have occurred in a Wright machine. The brothers' carefulness, which had borne fruit in their skill and sureness, had been markedly different from that of most other flyers. It was a cruel fate that served them, for their conservatism through eight years of work had never relaxed.

Wilbur's chief concern, after he was sure that Orville was safely on the road to recovery, was whether the accident had been due to a fault in the machine or to Orville's faulty operation. It was not until many months later that he found out that the propeller had broken.[39]

Despite his gnawing worry about Orville, Wilbur continued to fly in France, making records in mounting crescendo. In a conscientious manner typical of the rigid ethics of the brothers, he continued to do what he had come to France to accomplish, without giving in to his personal anguish.

By the end of September, Orville was out of danger. Chanute wrote reassuringly on October 7 to Wilbur, giving one of the rare descriptions available of Orville's pleasant personality, which attracted all who met him:

When I left Orville, September 30th (to meet my people in New York on return from Europe) he was pronounced quite out of danger and his broken leg had so far knitted that the surgeon told me that it would not be more than ⅛ shorter than the other. His temperature, which had been 101 4/5 part of the time, had become normal, and although he was still weak, (having been fed

[38] Adams, *Flug*, 83.

with liquid food) he had recovered his pluck and mental poise; the old genial smile had come back.

He had so endeared himself to all the Army Officers and men with whom he had come in contact, as well as to the hospital attendants, that they were eager to do all they could for him, but, of course, a military hospital is not as comfortable as one's own house.

At the Cosmos Club, where he had been staying, he had become very much liked and the members kept continually asking about him, only regretting the surgeon's orders prevented calling upon him.

Your Sister has been devotion itself. Fearing that he might lack something she stayed up at the hospital every night and deprived herself so much of sleep that I ventured to remonstrate with her about it. She then said that as the danger of complications seemed to be over that she would take better care of herself, go down to Washington to sleep and return to Dayton as soon as she felt that she could do so.

She has, of course, advised you that Orville will have to remain at the hospital about a month more and then can go home on crutches.

The newspapers have said that Mr. Weiler deems the first $100,000 practically won and has given an order for another $100,-000 worth of machines. I hope that you will occasionally find time to give me news of yourself.

Yours very truly,

One newspaper attributed Orville's psychological recovery to Chanute's encouragement and enthusiastic planning for the future. Noting that Chanute was the first to take his place at the bedside of the stricken aviator, the article went on to say that Chanute, now seventy-six years old, was the youngest man of his years at Fort Myer.

By October, Wilbur had begun to fly with various passengers, and in a few weeks he fulfilled that portion of his con-

---

[39] Chanute, "Recent Progress in Aviation," Smithsonian Institution 1910 *Annual Report*, reprinted from *Journal* of the Western Society of Engineers, Vol. XV (April, 1910), 150.

tract calling for two flights of fifty kilometers each, to be made within a week, carrying a passenger or a bag of sand equaling the weight of a passenger.[40]

This strenuous work was combined with the strain of worrying about Orville and the sorrow of being separated at this time. It was reflected in his looks, and Chanute wrote to Wilbur, after receiving a postal card which was evidently a photograph: "Dear me! How thin you have grown! Your Sister said you were emaciated and nervous but I had no idea it was to this extent."

The honor of flying with Wilbur Wright was eagerly sought for, and Wilbur gave short flights to over thirty passengers, including diplomats, aeronauts, and even, in spite of his conventionality, to women. Mrs. Hart O. Berg was his first woman passenger, but Leon Delagrange, on an exhibition tour in Italy a few months before had taken up the first woman passenger in the world, Mme Therese-Peltier.[41] Griffith Brewer noted admiringly that Wilbur never accepted payment for these flights.

Santos-Dumont appeared on the scene again, this time with his tiny monoplane soon to be known all over the world, the *Demoiselle*. This remarkable plane was so small that Santos-Dumont carried it, fully assembled, from Paris to St. Cyr in the rear of an automobile.[42] The *Demoiselle* was the lightest and most powerful of its kind yet to be developed. With his usual (or unusual) generosity and public spirit, Santos-Dumont later sold machines like this at cost, and refused to apply for patents on it.[43]

The French were really pressing hard on Wilbur's wings.

[40] *Automotor Journal* (London), Vol. XIII, No. 35 (August 29, 1908), 1152.

[41] This is another disputed "first." Some claim that Henry Farman, only a few days before the Delagrange-Peltier flight in Turin on July 8, 1908, had taken up the first woman passenger, Mlle P. van Pottelsberghe. This was during Farman's flights at Ghent.

[42] *Scientific American,* Vol. 99 (December 12, 1908), 433.

[43] Lougheed, *Vehicles of the Air,* 148.

Robert Esnault-Pelterie had made an excellent and speedy flight in June in his monoplane, but, because of faulty stability, the flight had ended in a crash. He continued to work on monoplanes, however, and increased their size.

Henry Farman, on October 30, made the first cross-country flight in history, covering in twenty minutes the seventeen miles from Chalons to Reims. This achievement opened a new era in the development of the airplane. On the following day, Louis Bleriot also made a cross-country flight. The French were clearly in the lead in this new angle, and were delighted by the progress of their flyers.

In contrast to their enthusiasm was Wilbur's attitude, as reported in the *Scientific American:* "[He] does not favor such spectacular performances as that of Farman, which, he claims, could not have been made save under ideal weather conditions and with the running of an extreme risk of accident."[44]

Soon after the cross-country flights of Farman and Bleriot, Wilbur began to try for altitude. On November 13, making his first official attempts to gain height, he won the prize of the Aero Club de France for altitude, reaching first 147.4 feet, and then 196 feet. By the middle of December Wilbur flew sixty-two miles in one hour, fifty-four minutes—a world record—and rose to a height of 360 feet—another world record.[45] Thus, in spite of the increased skill of the French flyers, Wilbur and his plane in 1908 led the world in flying.

By the end of October, the brothers had overcome their past difficulties and were able to look forward to an almost cloudless future. In America, Orville had been discharged from the hospital, and had received an extension of nine months for the delivery of his plane from the Secretary of War.

[44] *Scientific American,* Vol. 99 (November 21, 1908), 350.

[45] Lougheed, *Vehicles of the Air,* 478 ff.; Chanute, "Chronology of Aviation" and "Recent Progress in Aviation," Smithsonian Institution, 1910 *Annual Report,* 160–61, 150.

Herring was out of the competition: his plane was wrecked on October 28 on its first flight. Walter L. Brock,[46] who later became a famous flyer in England, worked for Herring in this period, and described his experiences. Brock joined Herring first in 1907, in a little shop on Broadway in New York, until Herring became too heavily involved in the stock market crash of 1907. Eventually Herring managed to raise more money in order to enter the United States Government competition, and Brock, attracted always by Herring's brilliance, left a good job and again worked for him. But Brock soon became discouraged, for Herring had too many ideas, and changed them so frequently that his designs were modified each day. According to Brock, Herring's ideas were always good, but his continual discarding of the old for a new and better plan prevented any consistent, consecutive work.

A different picture of Herring's personality, as well as serious, well-documented claims on Herring's behalf have been put forth by another American aviation pioneer, James V. Martin. Martin, important flyer and aeronautical inventor, worked for Herring in 1909, and states that Herring's first flight in a powered plane took place in 1889.[47] He describes with great sympathy Herring's subsequent efforts to build planes.

But the misfortunes that dogged Herring's life included even his efforts to qualify for this government test. In spite of his undoubted brilliance and keen, inventive mind, Herring's qualities as well as his career contrasted strongly with the Wrights'. His lack of persistency, for example, differed from the Wrights' careful tenacity of their ideas and their constant drive to reduce them to practice. Herring never delivered a plane to the government and, for the time being, offered no competition to the Wrights.

[46] A beautiful 1913 Morane-Saulnier type of monoplane is on display at the Chicago Museum of Science and Industry. It was built by Brock.

[47] James V. Martin, "When Will Merit Count in Aviation?" *The Libertarian* (Greenville, S. C.), Vol. III, No. 4 (October, 1924), 589 ff.

Santos-Dumont's *Demoiselle*

Leon Delagrange's Biplane

Henry Farman's Biplane

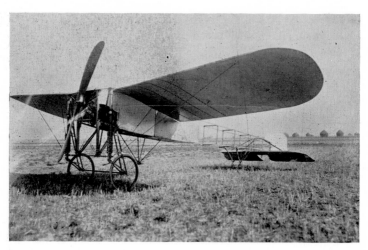

Bleriot Monoplane with 70 h.p. Gnome engine

In France, Wilbur was on the crest of the wave. He had fulfilled all but one of the terms of his contract—the instruction of three pupils in flying—for which he now began to make preparation. His popularity was undiminished, and he was the great man of the hour. His thoughts about his great success reflected the fatigue and nervous strain he was laboring under: he had had no time to himself during the previous three months, and on only a few occasions had he managed to get a rest by bicycling through the near-by woods.

Wilbur was homesick, and he longed to be back at Kitty Hawk. Although he appreciated the kindness and attentiveness of the French, he evidently felt alien in the midst of that friendly people.

On their side the French were so genuinely enthusiastic about Wilbur that they opened a public subscription for a testimonial. This spontaneous (so far as we know) gesture must have contrasted painfully in Wilbur's mind with the abortive effort that had been made in this country by James Means and Chanute to raise prize-money in a sufficiently large sum to induce the Wrights to give their first public flights here.

Means had started the idea in February, realizing how far ahead of the United States were the French flyers, and hoping to keep for this country the glory of the Wrights' first public exhibitions. Chanute agreed, and wrote to Means with his usual generosity, "Count me in."

Chanute, Means, and others tried to raise money for this aviation prize-fund, but they received pitifully few donations. The people were not interested in these overly mysterious Wright brothers. By early August, just before Wilbur began his spectacular exhibitions in France, Means and Chanute had to acknowledge that the aviation fund was a "mortifying" failure, and Chanute wound up the painful affair by offering to pay half the expenses which Means had incurred in this humiliating effort. Unfortunately, the Wrights knew of this attempt, and it probably did not diminish their already too strong feeling that they were without honor in their own country.

In this year of great personal triumph and world-wide fame there were also the beginnings of personal difficulties that were later to grow into large disagreements. Toward the end of the year, Charles Walcott, Langley's successor as secretary of the Smithsonian Institution, wrote to Chanute about the question of having Langley's machine rebuilt and test-flown in order to determine whether or not the failure in 1903 had been due to an inherent fault in the machine or to a defect in the launching device. Although it was not until 1914 that this resurrection of the Langley machine took place, Chanute's reply gave a judicious appraisal of this question—which is still the cause of heated arguments.

I have your letter of 16th asking whether in my judgment, it would be wise to make an attempt to fly with the Langley machine.

I have never seen this machine but I suppose that I understand it fairly well from descriptions.

My judgment is that it would probably be broken when alighting on hard ground and possibly when alighting on the water, although the operator might not be hurt in either case.

If the institution does not mind taking this risk and suitable arrangements can be made about the expense, I believe that it would be desirable to make the test, in order to demonstrate that the Langley machine was competent to fly and might have put our government in possession of a type of flying machine, which, although inferior to that of the Wrights, might have been evolved into an effective scouting instrument.[48]

Chanute's praise of the Wrights' machine is significant, for a second, more intimate problem than the above was begin-

[48] Dated November 20, 1908; in Charles G. Abbot, "The Relations Between the Smithsonian Institution and the Wright Brothers," Smithsonian *Miscellaneous Collections,* Vol. 81, No. 5 (September 29, 1928), 17–18.

ning to face the brothers: their relationship with Chanute, friend and adviser since 1900, was becoming increasingly strained and stiff. The blame rests equally on the usual well-meaning friends, who repeated to Chanute what they thought the Wright brothers had said, and vice versa; and on the "ubiquitous reporter," who had to find some copy to satisfy the great interest in the Wrights' personalities and history.

That question of priority, which dogs the steps of all scientific inquirers and plagues efforts at impartiality about the history of all inventions, was the basis of the trouble. The Wrights were always jealous of their title, emphasizing frequently that they had been the first inventors of the first successful heavier-than-air machine in the world. It could not, therefore, have been pleasing to them to be labeled, as frequently happened, "Chanute's pupils," or "followers of Chanute in the school of Lilienthal." To add fuel to the fire, their plane was increasingly often described as an adaptation of the Chanute 1896-97 glider, and men of the reputation of Charles M. Manly were quoted as saying that all inventors, here and abroad, had copied Chanute's machine. Manly named Farman and Delagrange as well as the Wright brothers, as examples of flyers who had profited so largely from Chanute's work, saying, according to the *New York Tribune* on July 1, 1908, " 'The truth is that Mr. Chanute gave them the great idea, and they have never, none of them, given to him the credit that is his due.' "

Many others blamed the brothers for their lack of vocal appreciation of Chanute's work. But still worse were the alleged interviews reported by prominent journals. "Wilbur Wright Opens Out a Little," was the heading of one, which continued in part:

. . . there are one or two points upon which Mr. Wright was unusually emphatic, and would appear to desire that greater prominence should be given. There is, it seems, a common impression that the Wrights were pupils of Octave Chanute, but so far from this being actually the case, Mr. Wilbur Wright states that neither he nor his brother ever met Chanute until the latter was attracted by the rumors of their experiments to visit them at Dayton.[49]

This statement was published first in France and then in England, although it was patently untrue that Chanute had been "attracted" to them "by rumors." It was unfortunate that such inaccurate articles were more interesting than the truth. The Wrights themselves, in their famous article in the *Century Magazine,* published only one month before, had stated clearly that Chanute first visited them in 1901 "at our invitation." Moreover, they acknowledged their indebtedness for Chanute's encouragement, if not for his ideas, saying:

When he [Chanute] learned that we were interested in flying as a sport, and not with any expectation of recovering the money we were expending on it, he gave us much encouragement.[50]

On his side, Chanute, although proud of his contributions to the art, was as careful in his private correspondence as in his frequent public speeches to give the Wrights credit for their achievements. A clear statement of his attitude was given by Chanute to M. Paul Renard of Paris, brother of the famous balloon pioneer, Colonel Charles Renard. This was in reply to Renard's letter describing the general enthusiasm in France for the Wrights, but deprecating the fact that so few seemed to remember that the Wrights were Chanute's pupils.

Chanute answered Renard's letter carefully, the first sentence striking the keynote of this thought: "As in almost all inventions, the latest aviators profited legitimately by the work of their predecessors." Giving credit to Wenham[51] for having been the first to propose the biplane form, Chanute

---

[49] *Automotor Journal* (London), October 24, 1908, 1382.

[50] Wright brothers, "The Wright Brothers' Aeroplane," *Century Magazine,* Vol. LXXVI, No. 5, (September, 1908), 645.

[51] F. H. Wenham first patented the two-surface construction in *1866* (English patent No. *1571*); in *1908* he wrote to Chanute: "I am now in my 85th year with plenty of kick in me still," and went on to say that he was designing a new air propeller! Unfortunately, Wenham died the following fall, in August, 1909.

then indicated briefly his own additions to Wenham's idea. He went on to emphasize the importance of the Wrights' contributions: their application of a motor to the biplane glider form; their propellers, which were superior to all others; and their engine, which was *"robuste et certain."* Most important, they had built their plane, engines, and propellers with their own hands, operated them by themselves and at their own risk and peril.

Chanute then described his relationship with Wilbur, starting with the first letter in May, 1900:

I answered cordially with many letters furnishing him with the information desired.

After having made the gliding experiments at Kitty Hawk in October, 1900, Wilbur Wright wrote me a long account and invited me to come to see him. I was present at part of his experiments in 1901–1902–1903–1904 and 1905, and we became intimately acquainted. In eight years we have exchanged about 200 letters, on the questions which arose and on the progress made; some day these letters will serve as part of the history of the conquest of the air, as well as two lectures given by Wilbur Wright at my invitation before the Western Society of Engineers in Chicago in September, 1901, and June, 1903.

The most important question, that of the exact contributions he had made to the Wrights' work, Chanute answered only inferentially. He had, however, indicated his contribution when mentioning the previous work of their predecessors.

Such calm appraisals of the past were not, however true they might be, good copy. Unfortunately, neither Chanute nor the brothers made determined efforts to correct the more frequent inaccurate articles that recurrently appeared. On one side, Chanute refused to capitalize his long friendship with them, and, an old man of seventy-six, would not climb on the band wagon now forming around the famous brothers. The Wrights, on their side, rarely rushed into print to correct errors, even when they were exceedingly angry.

The articles grieved Chanute and were a source of distress to the Wrights. Their correspondence made no mention of them at this time. When they did write about these misquotations, it was too late to repair the damage to their friendship. They continued to correspond until that time, for another year and a half, but the heart had gone out of their letters.

By the end of this year the brothers had triumphed in their undertakings. Other men, in similar positions, could be described as enjoying a complete success; to these two men, success meant increased emphasis on their work.

Wilbur, with all France at his feet, was not able either by his training or his own qualities to take advantage of the many-sided pleasures that life in Paris has always offered to those who welcome cultural and intellectual stimulation. Not for the Wright brothers were the gaiety and laughter of Paris, the vital art movements, the theaters, or music. Brought up to keep the Sabbath strictly, they could not understand the Continental Sunday, which is interpreted as a day when all can, and should, be happy. The pleasures of a glass of wine in a bistro were closed to them, for they never smoked or drank.

Of course the French noticed the Wrights' lack of worldly enjoyments and even their friends regretted the joys they were missing. One French admirer described Wilbur as "This ascetic, who is ignorant of practically everything in life."[52] Indeed, Wilbur himself said that the pursuit of happiness was futile. Their accurate biographer, Griffith Brewer, wrote: "Discussing happiness one day, Wilbur remarked that most enjoyment in life consisted of relief from discomfort. To try to be always comfortable and happy was therefore a mistake, for if one succeeded life became unbearably monotonous."[53] At the same time, Wilbur acknowledged to Heinrich

[52] Peyrey, *Les Oiseaux Artificiels,* 202.

[53] Brewer, "The Life and Work of Wilbur Wright," *The Aeronautical Journal* (London), Vol. XX, No. 79 (July–September, 1916), 132.

Adams that he would be completely "comfortable" at this time—if only Orville were with him.[54] In short, Wilbur was still homesick, in spite of all the honors and glories that were being heaped on him. Longing to be at Kitty Hawk, he nevertheless remained in Europe, and piled record on record flight. Having attained all that man could hope for on this sad and sinful earth—relief from discomfort—he asked Orville to join him in Europe, in order that he might be even more "comfortable."

With a sense of the dramatic unusual for the brothers, Wilbur made another record on the last day of the year: on December 31, 1908, staying in the air for two hours, twenty minutes, twenty-three seconds, Wilbur Wright won the coveted Michelin prize.[55] He covered a distance of seventy-seven miles by the official recording; the unofficial estimate was ninety miles. The press reported that Wilbur did not trouble to take possession of the trophy. But they also noted that he received the 20,000-franc prize-money.[56] The Wrights kept their purpose fixed on the business of aviation.

Wilbur ended this eventful year of 1908 in making preparations to teach three pupils, and waiting for Orville to join him.

[54] Adams, *Flug,* 79.

[55] Chanute, "Chronology of Aviation," Smithsonian Institution, 1910 *Annual Report,* 160–61.

[56] *L'Aérophile* (Paris), année XVII (January 12, 1909), 39.

CHAPTER XII

Alloyed Triumphs–1909

Even as a guest at the villa of Baron Celler he would sit silently during meals. "He throws out thirty words like an engine. Then he keeps silent, as though he had been turned off mechanically. After the end of the meal, and sometimes earlier, he gets up and leaves. His brother Orville always follows him. Orville's face expresses a slightly more benign feeling toward humanity. His accident has evidently led him back somewhat into contact with mankind."[1]

THIS WAS the impression given by the brothers in Italy in 1909 when they were at the height of their fame, as reported by their sympathetic German biographer, Heinrich Adams. These were the two most famous flyers in the world.

Another, complementary picture of Wilbur is given by an English admirer and friend, Lieutenant Colonel A. Ogilvie:

Wilbur . . . was not only a past-master on the subject of flying, a master willing and anxious to impart anything he knew, but also one who would give careful, painstaking and entirely unselfish consideration to any matter, however unimportant. I never knew him to give a hasty or ill-considered judgment about anything [sic] or any person.[2]

Orville and Katharine had joined Wilbur in France early in January. Orville was slowly recovering from his accident, and Katharine needed a rest from her faithful nursing of him through the dark days that followed the crash. Wilbur was carrying out his French contract to teach three men to fly, at

[1] Adams, *Flug,* 104.
[2] Lieutenant Colonel A. Ogilvie, "Wilbur Wright Lecture," *The Aeronautical Journal* (London), October, 1922, 381.

Pau. The flying field was again the gathering place of great and enthusiastic crowds, which were enhanced by the presence of King Edward of England, and King Alphonso XIII of Spain, as well as nobility and aeronauts from all over Europe.[3]

The fortunate men chosen to be Wilbur's first pupils were Count Charles de Lambert, Captain P. Lucas-Girardville, and Paul Tissandier. They learned fast: de Lambert had twenty-three lessons, totaling five hours, twenty-two minutes, seven and one-fifth seconds. Tissandier had seventeen lessons, totaling four hours, forty-two minutes; and Lucas-Girardville, twelve lessons, or two hours, fifty-eight minutes. Learning to fly, Wilbur believed, was like learning to bicycle: the youngest learned fastest. Wilbur, although certainly not a feminist, said that little girls were the aptest pupils; next in order came young boys, then young men, and last, older men.[4]

While at Pau, the Wrights were visited by many Italians who were eager to induce them to visit Italy, where the enthusiasm of the people for flying had been aroused in 1908 by Delagrange's exhibitions. Among the many visitors was the father of Mme Gabriel D'Annunzio. Having signed a contract which was reported to be for 50,000 francs, the Wrights left Pau after a few months for Italy.[5]

Once again they were honored by royalty, Wilbur's flights caused great excitement, and the Wrights were given an enthusiatic reception—and orders for their planes. According to contract, Wilbur taught two Italians, one army officer, Lieutenant Savoya, and one naval officer, Lieutenant Mario Calderera. Calderera, the youngest pupil, bore out Wilbur's theory by learning to fly faster than any of the others, achieving his mastery after the very short time of two and one-half hours in the air, made up of eighteen flights.[6]

[3] Peyrey, *Les Oiseaux Artificiels*, 214.
[4] Adams, *Flug*, 93.
[5] Peyrey, *Les Oiseaux Artificiels*, 216.
[6] Chanute, "Recent Progress in Aviation," Smithsonian Institution, 1910 *Annual Report*, 156; Adams, *Flug*, 105.

But his pupils sometimes worried Wilbur. Calderera smoked excessively in his opinion (as any smoking is too much for the taste of a non- or anti-smoker). Wilbur feared that Calderera's head was being turned by the adulation and flattery which were lavished on him. Shortly after the Wrights left Italy, Calderera did indeed have a bad accident. Writers of the time attributed it to his having lost consciousness while in the air.

Some time later Count de Lambert, Wilbur's first pupil, made a spectacular flight from Juvisy across Paris over the Eiffel Tower, and back to Juvisy. The French were particularly excited about this flight, which outlined in so startling a way the aeroplane in actual flight clearing the great height of their beloved *Tour Eiffel*. Orville was at the Juvisy flying field to greet de Lambert when he landed there.[7]

Their stay in Italy was limited to four weeks, for they were pressed by the fact that they must pass the United States Government tests and deliver their plane to the War Department by the end of June, to which time their contract had been extended.

Leaving Rome, they stopped at Le Mans a brief time only, where they were guests at a dinner given in their honor. But already their popularity in France had begun to wane. The gold of popular acclaim had begun to show its tarnish. The French were less enthusiastic now about the Wright brothers. The French aviators had intensified their efforts after seeing Wilbur's exploits, and they were themselves trying to equal or surpass his records.[8] Furthermore, the French had already developed a number of remarkable monoplanes which they believed had many advantages over the Wrights' biplane. Chief among these were Santos-Dumont's and Bleriot's mono-

7 *Scientific American*, Vol. 101 (October 30, 1909), 310.

8 Byron R. Newton, "Recollections of the Days When Wings Emerged," *U. S. Air Services*, Vol. XVII (January, 1932), 26; Adams, *Flug*, 107; *Westminster Gazette* (London), May 4, 1910, 11.

planes, and the *Antoinette* models produced by Voisin Brothers.

Particularly welcome, therefore, after the slight cooling off in France, was their enthusiastic reception in England, where they received the Gold Medal of the Royal Aeronautical Society, oldest aeronautical organization in the world.[9] They received also orders for their machines, which they arranged to have filled by the British firm of Short Brothers. They decided against forming an English company as yet, and thus they kept their English patents and their English business largely under their own control for a while longer.

After this brief stay in England, the Wrights started for home, feeling no apparent regret at leaving Europe. It is likely that they were aware that the current in France had begun to turn against them. A stronger element was the fact that they had been constantly homesick, in spite of the many honors heaped on them. Those who have suffered from nostalgia know that there is no cure for this real sickness other than to return home.

The Wrights came back with increased wealth, in improved health, and with accumulated honors and fame. In the latter part of his stay abroad, Wilbur had gained about twelve pounds. Orville was in excellent health and able to walk without a cane. Katharine had recovered from her worry and fatigue.

Their country welcomed them with extraordinary honors: New York gave them a rousing reception when they landed there. They went to Washington to receive from President Taft the gold medals awarded by Congress and by the Aero Club of America. They were awarded the first Langley Medal, established by the Smithsonian Institution. At this time there was nothing to be seen, not even a small cloud, in the bright, shining sky. They could have spent their days basking in the sun of popular acclaim.

9 Adams, *Flug*, 108.

But the Wrights resented the time spent on presentations and speeches, and were irritated that a good part of a week would have to be spent traveling to and from Washington to receive these honors. Dayton, Wilbur felt, had made their return an excuse for a two-day carnival of self-advertisement; and this was done in spite of their expressed distaste for the display.

However, as Chanute wrote them, they had brought it on their own heads. "I know," he wrote in June, "that the reception of such honors becomes oppressive to modest men and they would avoid them if they could, but in this case you have brought the trouble upon yourselves by your completing the solution of a world-old problem, accomplished with great ingenuity and patience at much risk of personal injury to yourselves."

These honors were piled on them just before the final tests of their plane for the United States Government. If there had been any suspicion that the War Department was forced into purchasing the plane because of their great fame, it was soon dispelled by the brilliance with which Orville passed the tests, and his achieving of new records with the plane.

In spite of the fact that they were the crowned kings of flying, the unfortunate idea spread and has since grown that the Wright brothers had been neglected in their own country. Always prone to easy self-criticism, the people of the United States began to beat their breasts in shame over what was represented to them as their "neglect of their own prophets." This impression has gained through the years, even after the United States had heaped one honor after another on the Wrights' sometimes unwilling heads. Actually this government was the first in the world to contract for a military airplane.[10] The Army Signal Corps (in which the Aeronautics

[10] U. S. House of Representatives, 70 Cong. 1 sess., *Hearings* . . . on H.R. 11273, 5; Abbott, "The Relations Between the Smithsonian Institution and the Wright Brothers," Smithsonian *Miscellaneous Collections*, Vol. 81, No. 5 (September 29, 1928), 2.

Division was included) contained men of vision who had had experience in aviation and who were aware of its possibilities. They were in advance of the country as a whole, which was shown when Congress in this year refused to appropriate the $500,000 requested by General James Allen for the development of military aviation. Some experts foresaw the future role of the airplane in warfare: A. A. Merrill, founder of the Boston Aeronautical Society in 1895, and its secretary and treasurer through 1912, wrote prophetically in 1909: "Flyers and men are cheap where it is a question of destroying battleships."[11] Thus, as early as 1909, began the argument of air power versus sea power.

Another prophetic statement was made by Hudson Maxim at this time, when he was giving an address in New York: "God will hereafter fight on the side that has the strongest flying machines and the most of them."[12]

The Wright brothers, busy with their travels and engrossed with their planes and business arrangements, were not vitally interested in these arguments. But their correspondence with Chanute, their published letters to Captain Ferber and to *L'Aérophile* in 1905, when they first offered their plane to governments for use in warfare, all show that they realized early that their chief selling point was war.

The interest abroad, particularly in France, was still in glaring contrast to the indifference of the public in the United States. Whereas aviation prizes totaling over $350,000 were offered by the beginning of 1909 in Europe, there was only one prize for aeronautics in the United States.[13] Actually, there were few in this country who had ever seen an airship, and even fewer had seen an aeroplane. The American public needed the sight of an aeroplane in flight to arouse its interest and enlist its support.

[11] *Scientific American*, Vol. 100 (January 23, 1909), 83.
[12] *Aeronautics* (New York), Vol. IV, No. 2 (February, 1909), 64.
[13] *Scientific American*, Vol. 100 (January 2, 1909), 6.

The Wrights were never aware of the importance of this natural curiosity to see them fly. They were not now, any more than they had been or would ever be, interested in exhibition flights, in making spectacular records *qua* records, or in competing for prizes. When Chanute wrote to Wilbur, "I told you in New York that you were making a mistake by abstaining from prize winning contests while public curiosity is yet so keen," Wilbur felt only scorn at the suggestion. They were entitled to great rewards because they were inventors, they felt; they would not become clowns competing in the clowning business. They were at this time contemptuous about exhibition flying, looking down on it as pandering to bloodthirsty crowds who wanted only to see accidents and crashes.

"I do not compete for trophies," Heinrich Adams quoted Wilbur as saying to him, "unless I can win them occasionally through those flights which I am obliged to make by my contracts."[14]

The brothers were insistent on the practical aspects of flying, not the spectacular.

Others, however, were preparing to fill this demand and to gratify the natural curiosity and desire of the people to see this new machine. The Wrights thus found, on their return from Europe, a tremendous activity in this country in aviation circles, which Chanute described in a letter of June 6, 1909, as "the feverish eagerness with which hundreds of experimenters have entered the field."

First among these was Glenn H. Curtiss, until recently a member of Bell's Association. Curtiss's first plane had been purchased in May of this year by the Aeronautical Society of New York (for a price reported as $5,000) and Curtiss gave the first exhibition flight in it on June 26, 1909.[15] A large crowd

[14] Adams, *Flug,* 76.

[15] Clara Studer, *Sky Storming Yankee,* 158; *Scientific American,* Vol. 100 (March 13, 1909), 203; (May 22, 1909), 387; U. S. House of Representatives, 74 Cong., 1 sess., Committee on Patents, *Hearings* "Pooling of Patents" (1935), 109.

of about two thousand people flocked out to Morris Park to watch the flight, for this was New York's first opportunity to see an American airplane make a public flight.

Immediately comparisons began to be made: It was noted, for instance, that Curtiss's speed of forty-six and seven-tenths miles per hour exceeded any ever made by the Wrights, although their engines had the same power. Curtiss took the next step in the development of flying—arranging to teach Charles F. Willard to fly this plane, with the idea that Willard would then tour the country. Willard was thus the first of those brilliant exhibition flyers who soon traveled all over the country and brought actual flying into the experience of all its people.

The Aeronautical Society of New York and its members were so active that they moved from Morris Park to a larger field at Mineola, Long Island. The members tried out their planes, and were glad to be able to borrow the Society's engine for their tests. Many of the members, including the Witteman brothers, Charles Kimball, and Morris Bokor, continued to develop their designs. Dr. Henry W. Walden built his *Walden III*, a pusher monoplane, which was later called the first successful American monoplane.

On the West Coast also there was great activity, auguring that section's future importance. The advantageous climate and geography of Southern California had been pointed out by Chanute as early as 1893, when he wrote, "The attention of designers of flying machines, who may want to test the merits of their devices upon a really adequate scale, is particularly directed to the vicinity of San Diego, California."[16]

In Los Angeles, the group of eager students who, under the inspiring leadership of H. LaV. Twining, had formally organized the Aero Club of California in 1908, were now raising funds for the successful launching of the international aviation meet to be held early in 1910. This was the second in

[16] Chanute, *Progress in Flying Machines*, 264.

the world and the first to be held in the United States. Warren
S. Eaton, a high-school boy and member of the club, had already started, with his brother, the famous Eaton Brothers Airplane Company. Eaton later designed and built the
plane in which Lincoln Beachey looped-the-loop, and already
in 1909 had begun to give flying lessons in connection with
his factory.

The Pacific Aero Club had been started in San Francisco
by Cleve F. Shaffer, owner of the first shop on the Pacific
Coast to sell aeroplane parts. He then went to Santa Anna and
became Glenn L. Martin's shop superintendent. There he met
Charles Healy Day, Martin's first chief engineer, and designed, built, and flew his tractor biplane powered with an
engine of his own design.

In Dayton, Walter S. Brookins was haunting the workshop of his neighbors, the Wright brothers, as he had been
doing since 1900. Now a young man, he hoped that the brothers would keep their old promise to him and teach him to fly.

Judging by the great advances suddenly shown in aeronautics, here and abroad, it seemed that the Wrights' flights
of 1908-1909 had opened a large reservoir of flying energy. It
was as if the ability to fly successfully had awaited the stimulation of seeing the Wrights fly. Now the dam had burst.
By the middle of 1909, men all over Europe and in this country
were flying, were building planes, and were setting new
records. The spotlight of world attention flitted from one
flyer to another, and from Europe to the United States and
back again to Europe, highlighting the Wright brothers whenever they flew, but focusing also on many others. Exhibition
flying was spreading to all countries in Europe, and flights
were made in Sweden and Russia, in Denmark and Romania.
Meets were scheduled for many centers—Berlin, Brescia, Spa,
Boulogne, Dieppe, Frankfort, Blackpool, and Juvisy.

France continued to be the center of this activity: Santos-

Wright Brothers' Plane, 1910

Official photograph, U. S. Army Air Corps

Harriet Quimby, first American woman to try for a pilot's license and first woman to fly the English Channel, April 26, 1912, receives instruction from Andrew Houpert at Moisant Aviation School, Garden City.

First Curtiss Flying Boat, January, 1912

Dumont, Bleriot, Farman, Louis Paulhan, Delagrange, Roger Sommer, Hubert Latham, Wilbur's French and Italian pupils, and, in turn, their pupils, were all making progressively better flights.

By the end of June the brothers finished the plane intended for the United States Government and took it to Fort Myer, Virginia, for the final tests. Now the spotlight focused there, for these tests, which had ended with Orville's accident in 1908, would either be passed, or finally failed.

The first trial was a failure. The brothers had made several changes in the plane in order to increase its speed, but had not yet familiarized themselves with this new machine. Congress adjourned so that its members might see the famous Wrights fly. But the brothers refused to try out the plane when a slight wind sprang up suddenly. This fear of such a small breeze made an unfavorable impression upon the audience (which no doubt welcomed any breeze), an impression which was deepened during the next few days when only a few feeble flights were achieved.

One aeronautical journal played up the fiasco of the first trials as follows:

... we had the tragi-comical spectacle of the "kings of the air," their brows fresh with the laurels of Dayton's great celebration, wearing the halo of surpassing records on two continents and strong in their renewed cooperation, doing—nothing, or, what was worse in the popular estimation, tinkering at a machine as if it had been the crudest experimental makeshift, and frightened by the lightest breath of air. ... In these surroundings their new fame became as uncomfortable as the halo of St. Anthony. To the aeronautical student the sight of the United States Senate leaving the tariff wrangle to make a pilgrimage to the scene of these *first* [*sic*] trials, was almost pathetic, under the excellent heating accomodations of the Washington landscape on a summer day.[17]

[17] Dienstbach, "The Revelations at Fort Myer," *American Aeronaut,* Vol. 1, No. 2 (September, 1909), 81.

The world did not stand still while Orville was trying to become familiar with the new machine. Louis Bleriot was making new records in France; Hubert Latham was preparing his attempt to fly the English Channel; Louis Paulhan beat Wilbur's altitude record; and Henry Farman made a record cross-country flight.

Orville soon succeeded in mastering the new plane. On July 20 he stayed in the air for one hour, twenty minutes, and forty-five seconds (unofficial timing), showing perfect control and making sharp turns at heights then considered great. Now the field at Fort Myer was the center of attraction for official and unofficial Washington. President Taft, the diplomatic corps, government employees, and the "social elite" of Washington, all flocked to Fort Myer. Orville continued to behave with the quiet dignity and the lack of fuss and self-importance characteristic of the brothers in their moments of triumph.

Orville's preparations for flying, as described in the following quotation, showed the absence of theatricalism which was the keynote of the Wrights' public appearances:

First he tied a piece of string around his cap so that it could not blow off. Next he calmly took off his coat, entirely unmindful of the thousands who were watching him, removed his cuffs . . . took his place in the pilot's seat, and uttered a laconic "Let her go" to his assistants.[18]

Four days after Orville's record on July 20, Glenn H. Curtiss won the *Scientific American* cup for the second consecutive year.

The next day the spotlight shifted over to France. Louis Bleriot, on July 25, flew the English Channel. He took off from Calais, passed the French destroyer which was waiting to guide him, and for ten minutes was out of sight of land and of his escorting ship. Bleriot had the then unique sensation of

18 Lester J. Maitland, *Knights of the Air*, 18–19.

being alone in the universe. More practically, he had no compass or any other instrument to guide him, and could fly only straight ahead at about forty miles an hour. Although he tried to allow for a strong southwest wind estimated at twenty miles per hour, he went several miles off his course.

Bleriot finally came into sight of the shores of England. He was guided to a landing place by another Frenchman on the shore, who was waving the French flag.[19] Bleriot had achieved the twin feats of flying across water, and from one country to another. This flight aroused enormous popular excitement.

The distance which he covered—somewhere between twenty-five and thirty-two miles—was not considered large, even at that time. But the fact of a flight from France to England was indeed a demonstration of the shrinking of national boundaries. The general reaction was great enthusiasm for this new "first," which seemed to open a new horizon. To a few people, Bleriot's flight was a disquieting omen of the future.

It is more than likely that the Wrights could have flown the Channel several years before this, for already in 1905 they had flown twenty-four miles, and in 1908 Wilbur had covered about seventy-seven miles. But they had not done so, and Bleriot had. Thus Bleriot's success not only increased his fame (and his accumulation of prizes as well), but, more than any previous flight, it awoke the public to a sudden awareness of the diminution of national boundaries and the practical development of flying.

An added feature of Bleriot's success was that he had made the flight in a monoplane, powered by a V-shaped, Anzani engine. Thus the Wright biplane was opposed by Bleriot's small Number XI monoplane.[20] The cheapness of the French

[19] Lougheed, *Vehicles of the Air*, 423; Zahm, *Aerial Navigation*, 290–91; *Scientific American*, Vol. 101 (August 7, 1909), 88.

[20] Lougheed, *Vehicles of the Air*, 281; Zahm, *Aerial Navigation*, 290.

monoplanes—Bleriot's selling for $2,400, and Santos-Dumont's *Demoiselle* for around $1,500—was another noteworthy fact.

Two days after Bleriot's flight, on July 27, the spotlight shifted back to Fort Myer. Orville, with Lieutenant Frank P. Lahm as his passenger, broke Wilbur's previous record by flying one hour, twelve minutes, thirty-five seconds (official timing), and covering about fifty miles.[21] Since the government specification was for only one hour's flight, this test was successfully hurdled.

Three days later Orville made the final official flight for the government contract: flying ten miles across country, with Lieutenant Benjamin D. Foulois as his passenger, Orville made a speed of 42.25 miles per hour. The requirement had been for only 40 miles an hour.[22]

The Wright plane had thus, by the end of July, passed all the government tests.

By his speed of 42.25 miles per hour, Orville earned a bonus of $5,000 over the bid price of $25,000, making a total cost to this government of $30,000. "There can be no criticism that the Wrights have failed in good business sense at every stage of their public career," Dienstbach remarked (but he was a friend of Herring).[23] Albert F. Zahm wrote later, mentioning the fact that the War Department had granted the Wrights three extensions of time for the delivery of their plane: "It was remarked that the War Department could easily drop these procrastinated experiments and buy a practical aeroplane in the open market for $5,000."[24]

In spite of these overtones, the fact was that the United States War Department had purchased a successful airplane, one "which is without doubt," the *Scientific American* commented, "the premier machine of the kind in the world to-

21 *Scientific American*, Vol. 101 (August 7, 1909), 88.
22 *Ibid.*
23 Dienstbach, "The Revelations at Fort Myer," *American Aeronaut*, Vol. I, No. 2 (September, 1909), 80.
24 Zahm, *Aerial Navigation*, 278.

day." "In its own field of strictly bird-like flight," Dienstbach wrote in the *American Aeronaut,* "the Wright machine seems like perfection."[25]

Again attention shifted to Europe, where the international aviation meet at Reims was held late in August. The French were making great strides with their monoplanes, but the only American entrant, Glenn H. Curtiss, flew a biplane. After arriving at Reims, Curtiss sent a postal card to the aeronautics editor of the *Scientific American,* saying: "Bleriot here with 5 machines one 80 H.P. otherwise I am fastest I think. G.H.C."[26]

Curtiss was right. Bleriot was his most formidable opponent. Their close competition was shown in the speed race for the James Gordon Bennett trophy. Curtiss was the first winner of the trophy—and in a biplane—but he beat Bleriot only by the narrow margin of five and three-fifths seconds.

While Wilbur was preparing to teach two American army officers to fly, Orville went to Germany, and there gave one of the last public demonstrations of the Wrights' great abilities as pilots. Orville's trip to Germany was probably part of the contract with the Wright Flying Machine Company (*Flugmaschine Wright, GmbH,* Berlin) formed late in May of this year. The backers of the German Wright Company included principal arms manufacturers and financial groups of Germany: Krupp, Hugo Stinnes, Ludwig Loewe and Company, and Allgemeine Elektrizitäts Gesellschaft. The Wrights assigned their patent rights in Germany to the new company.[27]

A cable, sent to the *Chicago Tribune* from Berlin on September 4, 1909, while Orville was flying there, stated: "The German Wright Company will be prepared to deliver machines after October 1st. The machines sell at $5,000 apiece

[25] Dienstbach, "The Revelations at Fort Myer," *American Aeronaut,* Vol. I, No. 2 (September, 1909), 86.

[26] *Scientific American,* Vol. 101 (September 11, 1909), 180.

[27] Adams, *Flug,* 133; *Scientific American,* Vol. 100 (May 29, 1909), 381, 403; *ibid.,* Vol. 102 (January 1, 1910), 8.

and anybody acquainted with the incredibly simple construction of the Wright machines can figure out for himself that each machine at this figure represents a handsome profit for the owners of the German patents."

Orville's flights were witnessed by the German royal family, and he took up the Crown Prince for a short one. The flights were notable, as was always true of the Wrights. With Captain A. Englehardt as his passenger, Orville beat his own record by flying one hour, thirty-five minutes, forty-seven seconds. Then he tried for altitude, and after several flights, early in October made an unofficial record of over 1,600 feet.[28]

In this country, while Orville was returning home from Europe, Wilbur and Glenn Curtiss were in direct, although veiled competition. The Hudson-Fulton Celebration in New York City was to include flights by these two prominent American flyers. Curtiss, returned home after winning prizes in Italy as well as in France, signed a contract to fly up the Hudson River from Governors Island to Grant's Tomb, and back. Wilbur had not yet committed himself to a specific course, but was expected to make equally spectacular flights.

Their juxtaposition must have been a strain on the two men. In August the Wright brothers had brought a suit in equity against the Aeronautical Society of New York to restrain it from further exhibition of its Curtiss plane, on the grounds that it infringed their patents. But the Aeronautical Society was protected by its contract with Curtiss, according to a statement by Lee S. Burridge, president, which made Curtiss the real defendant. The ball of accumulating lawsuits had been started rolling.[29]

At first both Curtiss and Wilbur were prevented from flying in the Hudson-Fulton celebration by bad weather. Finally Curtiss made a few very short flights before leaving for St.

[28] *Scientific American,* Vol. 101 (October 2, 1909), 239; *ibid.* (October 16, 1909), 274.

[29] *New York World,* August 20, 1909.

Louis. Wilbur, who was based on Governors Island, made one flight, circling the Statue of Liberty. A good deal was made of this flight and of its symbolism, for here was Wilbur Wright, whose public demonstrations of flying had hitherto all been made in France, gracefully paying tribute to that country by circling its famous gift to America.

Wilbur succeeded in making a second flight—from Governors Island to Grant's Tomb and back again. But his third attempt was cut short by the failure of his engine. Wilbur remarked that the machine was an old one he had used at Kitty Hawk, and added that he was opposed to exhibition flights even though he had made this one exception.[30] He then returned to College Park, Maryland, where he was teaching Lieutenants Frank P. Lahm and Frederic E. Humphries.

Although Wilbur's twenty-one-mile flight up the Hudson River and back was a fine exhibition, and New York was very enthusiastic over it, nevertheless the flying part of the Hudson-Fulton celebration was unsatisfactory as a demonstration of the possibilities of the airplane, even as that stage of its development.[31]

Furthermore, the rivalry over records and meets and prizes was now becoming complicated by real business competition. Already in March a preliminary announcement had been made of the forming of a $300,000 corporation. Cortlandt Field Bishop, president of the Aero Club of America, was organizing this company for the manufacture of aeroplanes, gliders, and balloons. This was to be the Herring-Curtiss Company, for both Herring and Curtiss held large interests in it. Herring was to assign to the company his American patents, when issued, "upon automatic stability devices, etc." The planes were to sell for $7,500, and gliders for $600. The factory was to be at Hammondsport (Curtiss's home), and the famous

30 *Scientific American,* Vol. 101 (October 23, 1909), 290.

31 Chanute, "Chronology of Aviation," Smithsonian Institution, 1910 *Annual Report,* 160–61; *Scientific American,* Vol. 102 (February 19, 1910), 259.

Captain Thomas S. Baldwin was to head the airship department.

Once more the Wright brothers were faced with the competition of Augustus M. Herring, and their suits against the Herring-Curtiss Company and Glenn H. Curtiss were to form the main thread of aviation history for nearly a decade. Herring's statement in his letter to them, foreseeing in 1904 the probability that their patents would overlap and would lead to expensive lawsuits, was about to be fulfilled.

One more step remained to be taken before the lawsuits burst upon the aeronautical world. This came in November, 1909, with the formal announcement of the formation of the Wright Company, incorporated in Albany, New York.

Wilbur was president, Orville and Andrew Freedman the vice-presidents, and Alpheus S. Barnes was the secretary and treasurer. The executive committee, which was most important in managing the affairs of the company, did not include Orville, but was composed of Andrew Freedman, chairman, Russell A. Alger, August Belmont, Cornelius Vanderbilt, and Wilbur Wright.

The Wrights had indeed incorporated themselves with the important financiers of the day. In addition to the brothers, the directors were Russell A. Alger, August Belmont, Edward J. Berwind, Howard Gould, Morton F. Plant, Allan A. Ryan, Theodore P. Shonts, Robert Collier, Andrew Freedman, Cornelius Vanderbilt, and Pliny W. Williamson.[32]

The press reported this company as part of a move to form an international trust. One paper said: "With basic patents in this country, Europe, Australia, and South America, covering everything believed to be conceivable in connection with the making of an aeroplane, the Wrights and Mr. Flint [Charles R. Flint, described in the same paper as "formerly head of the U. S. Rubber trust"] believe they have a monopoly

[32] *Aeronautics* (New York), Vol. VI, No. 1 (January, 1910), 11.

of the business."[33] Another said, "The syndicate, which will practically control the aviation of the world. . . ."[34]

The Wrights themselves regarded the formation of the American company from an entirely different angle: the company had bought from them their American business, paying them what they considered a satisfactory amount in cash plus 40 per cent of the stock, and also a promise to pay a royalty on each machine built. A general manager was to have charge of the business, and they themselves would supervise it only generally. Although the formation of the company had taken up much time, now they hoped they could spend most of their time on experimental work. Here was the old cry and hope of the brothers, which again would be largely interfered with by practical questions.

Now the lawsuits would rob them of their hope, for they were preparing for the suit against Herring and Curtiss. Wilbur was clearly irritated by Herring's claims that he had made prior inventions as long ago as 1894.

The Wright brothers had indeed grown apart from Chanute. Their earlier reliance on his advice and encouragement had disappeared; their roads went in opposite directions. The Wright brothers were businessmen in aviation; Chanute was still the scientist, focusing on the progress of the world. He had not forgotten the tables they compiled in 1901–1902 with his help, and the fact that these tables were never published. In February of this year Chanute wrote to Alexander Graham Bell mentioning the tables in part as follows: "In point of fact the success of the Wrights is partly based upon a series of experiments with 41 different forms of surface and 5 or 6 resulting tables (which I assisted in computing) from which they derived the best shapes for sustaining surfaces and propellers. I have all this information but I consider it confidential. The Wrights . . . subsequently concluded not to make this informa-

[33] *Chicago Tribune,* September 4, 1909.
[34] *Chicago Record Herald,* November 22, 1909.

tion public until they had realized a fortune by including it in the sales of their patents. I hope that they are now in a fair way to do this."

Chanute's last letter to the Wrights in 1909 made no comment on the formation of the Wright Company; it disregarded the news of the lawsuits; and it made no mention of any business details. It merely wished the whole Wright family a very happy New Year, from a man who was seventy-seven years old, engaged, once again, in preparing a paper for the December meeting of the American Association for the Advancement of Science.

By the end of 1909 the possibility of infringing the Wright patents had become a bugbear to the builders and flyers of planes in the United States and in Europe. Pending lawsuits were an inhibiting fear to new aviation companies. When the Wrights appealed for an injunction to restrain Glenn H. Curtiss and the Herring-Curtiss Company from exhibiting or manufacturing their planes, the bomb had fallen. And when the Wright Company then applied for an injunction to restrain Louis Paulhan from flying in this country, the question of priority of invention took on an international aspect.

Paulhan was scheduled to make flights in his Farman and Bleriot machines at the International Aviation Meet in Los Angeles in January, 1910, and at other exhibitions. But he was served with the legal notice of this suit as he stepped off the boat in New York.[35] Soon after, the Wright Company was awarded preliminary injunctions in both cases. This was an unusual legal procedure, since the validity of the patents in question had not yet been settled by legal action.[36] Both Curtiss and Paulhan appealed against the injunctions.

Although Paulhan fulfilled his engagements and made

[35] *Flight* (London), Vol. II (January 8, 1910), 22; *Daily Mail* (London), January 5, 1910.

[36] Charles B. Hayward, *Aeronautical Practice, Part II*, 68.

notable flights in this country, he had to post heavy bonds to protect the Wrights' interests. Meanwhile, the effects of the lawsuits, and particularly the injunction against the use of the French biplanes, caused a wave of criticism against the Wright brothers. Once again they were the subjects of international controversy.

Sir Hiram Maxim assured British inventors that they had nothing to fear, for they had available to them, alone among the countries in the world, he said, all the patents needed to build a flying machine "without borrowing inventions from other countries."[37] In France it was recalled that Wilbur had been disagreeably frank, after his arrival there in 1908, in expressing his belief that all successful French planes infringed his patents.

In a letter written probably in 1910, Wilbur said: "The so-called marvelous advance of French invention in the last year has consisted almost entirely in copying more and more closely the main features on which our patent is based, and that is exploited sensationally in moneymaking shows. We think the advancement of this art will not suffer greatly if these inventors are compelled to do some real experimenting and inventing instead of step by step bringing their method of lateral balance closer each day to an exact copy of ours."[38]

In America Glenn H. Curtiss delighted a large group of dinner guests by telling the following story:

"Orville," cries Wilbur, running out of doors excitedly, "look! Here's another aviator using our patent!"

"He certainly is!" shouts Orville. "That's our simultaneous warping and steering movement to a T!"

"Call a cop!" screams Wilbur. "Get another injunction!"

But Orville, who had looked up through his binocular, laid his hand gently on his brother's arm.

"Come on back to work, Wilbur," he said. "It's a duck."

[37] Maxim, *Artificial and Natural Flight*, 171–72.
[38] Studer, *Sky Storming Yankee*, 201.

Once more the Wrights had to postpone their hope of retiring to do experimental work. Again they put off their studies of theoretical questions; they had no time to prepare their important tables for publication. They had to follow their own emphasis, which had always been on the practical aspects of the aeroplane. From now on they were engulfed by their business; they were involved in the maze of lawsuits which took up so much time and energy that Wilbur's health, always dependent on out-of-doors living, suffered severely.

CHAPTER XIII

Incorporation of the Messrs. Wright

WILBUR AND ORVILLE had held the attention of the world for two years, 1908 and 1909. For these two brief years they reached the heights of fame. From now on, three possible courses of action were open to them: to continue with their flights and hold against all competition their position as the most successful flyers in the world; or to devote their energies to the development of their business and the defense of their patent rights; or to retire from their various business obligations and pursue the study of various scientific questions, of which they had only scratched the surface.

About the question of exhibition flying they had long since formed a definite decision: They would not become mountebanks and circus performers. This was consistent with their past actions, for they had never been interested in flying merely for display purposes.

In January, 1910, the Wright Company was awarded the temporary injunction against Curtiss and the Herring-Curtiss Company, a similar injunction against Louis Paulhan was about to be granted, and the preparation of the lawsuits did not seem likely to consume too much time and energy. They might, therefore, be able to avoid choosing between the second and third possibilities; it might be feasible to carry on simultaneously their own experiments and studies, to develop certain aspects of their business, such as testing out new machines and forming schools, as well as to prepare for the legal trials.

Occasionally a small doubt of their legal course crept into the Wrights' minds, as, for example, when Wilbur read an

223

alleged interview with Chanute published in the *New York World* of January 17, 1910, which was headlined as follows:

DR. CHANUTE DENIES
WRIGHT FLYING CLAIM
Declares Brothers Were Not First
by Many Years to Discover
Balance Principle
HAS TOLD THEM THEY ARE
WASTING TIME IN SUITS
"Father of Aeronautics" Says
the Strongest Point Attacked Is Protected
by Patents

Wilbur was worried about this and previous newspaper interviews reporting that Chanute doubted the originality of their claims, and wondered why Chanute had changed his mind about their control system since he first saw it in 1901. Wilbur considered it strange that no one had at first denied that it was their own invention; but only when competitors were faced with the legal consequences of the Wright patent did the search begin for prior patents and discoveries. The Wright system of wing warping was now being used almost universally, the brothers believed, and they believed also that they had been the first in the world to invent, use, and demonstrate it. The world was, therefore, in their debt, legally and morally.

However, Wilbur and Orville were concerned by newspaper articles such as the above, and wished to know whether anything had ever been printed which they had not seen that might lessen their claims. They would appreciate knowledge of any such information, even if this would prove that they were legally wrong, for it might be able to prevent their getting in too deep financially with their lawyers.

Wilbur was well aware of the extent to which an inventor might become involved in expensive litigation. His friend

Griffith Brewer indicated Wilbur's attitude in the following humorous anecdote:

Discussing the relative costs of Patent actions in America and in England, Wilbur gave me a humorous example of a Patent Attorney's quotation of the probable costs that would be incurred. On the patentee asking him how much it would cost to bring an action for infringement against an alleged infringer, the attorney replied by putting the question, "Well, how much have you got?" On the inventor giving an estimate of his realisable assets, the lawyer replied: "Well, that's just the amount the action will cost you."[1]

In a clear and lucid statement Chanute wrote to Wilbur on January 23, 1910, giving his opinion of the Wrights' claims:

Dear Mr. Wright:—

Being misdirected, your letter of 20th was somewhat late in reaching me. I return the envelope.

The clipping which you enclose (returned herewith) is the first which I have seen from the New York World, referring to myself. I shall be glad to see the others.

This interview, which was entirely unsought by me, is about as accurate as such things usually are. Instead of discussing it, I prefer to take up the main principles at issue.

I did tell you in 1901 that the mechanism by which your surfaces were warped was original with yourselves. This I adhere to, but it does not follow that it covers the general principle of warping or twisting wings; the proposals for doing this being ancient. You know, of course, what Pettigrew and Marey said about it. Please see my book, page 97, for what D'Esterno said of the laws of flight; the 3rd being torsion of the wings and the 6th being torsion of the tail. Also, page 106, Le Bris, rotary motion of the front edge of the wings. The original sources of information are indicated in foot notes. I did not explain the mechanism because I had not the data.

When I gave you a copy of the Mouillard patent in 1901 I think I called your attention to his method of twisting the rear of the wings. If the Courts will decide that the purpose and results were

[1] Brewer, "The Life and Work of Wilbur Wright," *The Aeronautical Journal* (London), Vol. XX, No. 79 (July–September, 1916), 134.

entirely different and that you were the first to conceive the twisting of the wings, so much the better for you, but my judgment is that you will be restricted to the particular method by which you do it. Therefore it was that I told you in New York that you were making a mistake by abstaining from prize winning contests while public curiosity is yet so keen, and by bringing suits to prevent others from doing this. This is still my opinion and I am afraid, my friend, that your usually sound judgment has been warped by the desire for great wealth.

Wilbur was stung by the last sentence and particularly by the phrase that they were moved "by the desire for great wealth." He felt that no one else who knew them had ever accused them of being mercenary, and that their actions had a moral basis: they had benefited the world by their arduous labors and by the financial and physical risks they had taken during the six years from 1900 to 1906. They had given to the world the successful solution of a centuries-old problem; therefore, the world was in their debt!

Emphatically Wilbur insisted that the lawsuits were merely a worldly expedient to force the world to acknowledge its debt. He insisted also that the Wrights had had no wish or intention to exploit their patents commercially, but had done so only when all other efforts to make money had failed because of envy and jealousy. And why should Chanute deny that they were entitled to a return as inventors, but concede them the right to collect money by circus performances?

Moreover, as Wilbur wrote in a letter at this time justifying their course:

The pretence that we are endeavoring to prevent others from doing anything to advance the art of flying is absolutely untrue. We have never taken legal steps against any man unless he eventually tried to make money for himself by parading our particular invention without compensation to us. No man who confined himself to the development of the art has been molested by us.

Chanute's point of view was as far as possible from that of

WRIGHT BROTHERS
1127 W THIRD STREET
DAYTON, OHIO

20 Jan 1910

Dear Mr. Newton,

We really do not know what the future of human flight will be. It will depend upon how much money will be available for experimental purposes. If the profits resulting from the present public enthusiasm are awarded to individuals who are interested in flying only as a show business, and who have no intention of spending it or any part of it in developing the art for the art's sake, the advance will be slower than if the profits are put into the hands of people who are interested in the future usefulness of flying machines more than in immediate spectacles, and who will spend a large part of the receipts in experimenting for the purpose of making flying something more than a mere show business. We think the profits of flying ought to bear the burdens of such experiments. The greatest problem in this art today is to find a satisfactory method of conserving the financial flood of today in such a way as to make irrigation possible when the dry season comes again.

Yours truly,
Wilbur Wright.

From U. S. Air Services, *December, 1913*
Reproduced by permission

THE WRIGHT BROTHERS, 1910
Orville is at the left, Wilbur at the right

the Wrights. He had never expected a return from his decades of labor, but had spent those years in an effort to further the art of flying. Chanute had not even expected to make money from the sale of his book, the basic source on aeronautical inventions. (Published in 1894, this book is now a rare item, eagerly sought for by collectors.) Twelve years after it had been published, in December, 1906, and when it was still the standard work on the history of aeronautics, Chanute wrote to his publisher, saying: "I, for one, feel that the reward has been fully as great as I expected. I advised printing only 1,000 copies and I believe you have sold nearly twice that."

The Wrights and Chanute had indeed reached an impasse. If he had achieved nothing else, his point of view marked Chanute as a scientist. And if the Wrights had failed in their efforts to make their aeroplane into an industry, their point of view would still have marked them as businessmen in aviation, for a return on effort is the purpose of commerce.

That they realized the larger aspects of financial returns from aeronautical activity is shown by a letter written by Wilbur at this time, and reproduced opposite page 226. It reveals their feeling against the "show business" of exhibition flying, as compared with their constant desire for further serious experimentation.[2]

Probably the terms under which the Wrights had ceded their patents to their companies obligated them to defend legally these patent rights. But in addition, the brothers were sure of their own moral rightness, and they were prepared to defend their moral, and legal, rights with a wholehearted belief in their cause.

Many of Chanute's old friends had died: Langley and Cabot in 1906, and Wenham in 1908. Captain Ferber was

[2] This letter was published also in Studer, *Sky Storming Yankee,* p. 201, but there it was preceded by three other paragraphs which emphasized the fact that Wilbur was justifying their lawsuits. The second paragraph given in Studer is on p. 221, and the third paragraph on p. 226 above.

killed late in 1909 while trying to fly across the Channel. Moedebeck died early in 1910. Chanute missed his comrades in aeronautics.

Now seventy-eight years old, Chanute began to feel his age but was able to continue with his large correspondence, and even went to Boston early in January, 1910, to attend a dinner given in his honor. Wilbur and Orville were also at this dinner, having looked forward to meeting Chanute there. Unfortunately, this was one of the rare occasions on which Wilbur was persuaded to make a speech—unfortunately for its effect on Chanute, the guest of honor.

A few weeks later Chanute described what he understood Wilbur to have said at this occasion, writing to Wilbur as follows:

If, as I infer from your letter, my opinions form a grievance in your mind, I am sorry, but this brings me to say that I also have a little grievance against you.

In your speech at the Boston dinner, January 12, you began by saying that I "turned up" at your shop in Dayton in 1901 and that you then invited me to your camp. This conveyed the impression that I thrust myself upon you at that time and it omitted to state that you were the first to write to me in 1900, asking for information which was gladly furnished, that many letters passed between us, and that both in 1900 and 1901 you had written me to invite me to visit you, before I "turned up" in 1901. This, coming subsequently to some somewhat disparaging remarks concerning the helpfulness I may have been to you, attributed to you by a number of French papers, which I, of course, disregarded as newspaper talk, has grated upon me ever since that dinner and I hope that in future, you will not give out the impression that I was the first to seek your acquaintance, or pay me left handed compliments, such as saying that "sometimes an experienced person's advice was of great value to younger men."

Wilbur did not deny that this was the gist of his speech. But he could not understand why Chanute should object to

anything he had said in Boston. He had not intended to imply
either that Chanute had taken the initial step in their acquaintance, or that he had not done so.

Then, as usually happens when tardy attempts are made to
articulate long-suppressed grievances, Wilbur dug up various
grudges that the brothers had cherished, harking back to 1902.
They had long been irritated by press reports describing them
as Chanute's pupils and even as his financial retainers. A few
years before, Wilbur had mentioned his anger to Chanute,
who had indignantly denied his responsibility for these
phrases. When Wilbur later went to France, he found there a
general belief that Chanute had given the Wrights all their
ideas, had lent them his glider, and had even furnished them
with money; and that they had contributed only mechanical
ability—and the Wrights always resented being called mechanics.

Contrary to Chanute's impression, Wilbur apparently had
not replied publicly to these statements in the press, since he
had not wanted to appear to belittle Chanute. He and Orville
had been upset, however, by Chanute's neglect to correct
these reports of their relationship or to testify to the independence of their work. But they thought that Chanute had
probably found it difficult to state exactly what he had contributed to their success. For they, too, had had enormous
difficulty in formulating the exact boundaries of their indebtedness to Chanute.

The difficulties which had blocked their friendship for
several years would, they hoped, be straightened out, for they
did not desire to fall out with a person for whom they would
wish to keep a sentiment of gratitude. In order to clear up the
situation, they suggested that Chanute and they together could
issue a statement which would clearly define what they all
knew to be true.

Chanute did not reply. His health had begun to fail at this
very time. To James Means he described this winter: "I regret

to say that I am not well. I remained shut in the house all winter and find myself stale. I am going South next week to loaf in the open air for a couple of weeks."

In the meantime the Wrights had continued with the lawsuits. Chanute received a letter and a copy of Wilbur's affidavit from Israel Ludlow, lawyer and aeronautical inventor with whom he had corresponded intermittently since 1895. Chanute wrote to Ludlow on February 25, giving a restrained opinion about this affidavit:

I have your favor of the 21 inst. I do not think that Mr. Wilbur Wright was justified in stating in his affidavit that the method of controlling the equilibrium by warping or twisting the wings was "unknown to" myself, although I admit that when writing those "conclusions" in 1893 I attached minor importance to the flexing of wings mentioned in my book on page 75, 2nd paragraph. . . . Nor, obviously, could I then (1893) mention the experiment of Mouillard in 1896, nor his patent of 1897, which latter provides for a method of flexing the rear of the wings which may serve in controlling the lateral balance, although the object stated is to provide for the horizontal steering. I gave a copy of that patent to Mr. Wilbur Wright in 1901.

Ludlow sent on to Chanute another affidavit, writing,

I feel very much as you do concerning Wright's statements, in fact even more strongly, for what he wrote was mild compared to what he allowed his counsel to say before the court.

It is not pleasant for a man with a knowledge of the history of aeronautics and a sense of values in connection with it, to hear Octave Chanute referred to as an "amiable old gentlemen" [sic] before a Judge of the Court of the United States.

I have been unable to ascertain whether the Wrights warped their wings prior to your arrival in Kitty Hawk but assume that they did.

I would appreciate your opinion on the enclosed affidavit.

Always refusing to become involved in a controversy about the Wrights (and Ludlow was counsel for Louis Paulhan and thus an opponent of the brothers), Chanute replied, on March 18, 1910: "I regret to say that my health is not good, and that I do not feel equal to discussing the Wright affidavit you were good enough to send me. Shall I send it back?"

Chanute's health did not improve.

The following month, in April, Wilbur made an attempt to articulate to Chanute the differences between them, and to express his desire to clear up these differences. Sadly the Wrights faced the fact that they had few close friends. They did not, therefore, easily lose those few. They realized that their intimacy with Chanute had been diminishing in the past year, but they had known only from Chanute's letter of January 23 that he as well as they had been cherishing hurt feelings. They had tried to be frank, in order to preserve this friendship which was in danger of ending with bitterness. They still hoped that their differences arose from expressions of facts, not from facts *per se*.

The Wrights were sincerely grateful to the friend of their first, struggling efforts. But the hard feelings that the brothers felt, and that, they now realized, Chanute also felt, must be, they hoped, cured somehow. Almost naïvely the brothers felt that this cure might lie in working out with Chanute a public statement of the true facts of their relationship with him.

There was no reply from Chanute. Never naïve, he was, rather, a subtle man of great understanding and vast experience. The gap between his philosophy, as shown by his long, busy life, and the path chosen in the past few years by the Wright brothers could not be bridged by a mere public statement. Actually, this important friendship, which had started ten long years before, was now ending; and it was ending in sadness and pain.

Chanute went to Europe in this summer, to try to regain his health. He was given great honors all over the Continent, and planned to go to England to receive the Gold Medal of the Royal Aeronautical Society. However, in August he became ill with pneumonia. By October he had improved sufficiently to return home to Chicago. But the recovery was brief; on November 24, 1910, Octave Chanute died.

He was honored by the world as the foremost authority on the history of aeronautics and as a pioneer who had made valuable contributions to the science. He was regretted sadly by the world as the man who had always helped all other pioneers in their efforts.

Wilbur wrote an article in tribute to Chanute. His encouragement of the Wright brothers "to persevere in their experiments," Wilbur wrote, and "his missionary trip to France in 1903" had altered "the entire history of progress in flying."[3] These words showed that Wilbur had real difficulty in determining the exact degree of their indebtedness. The Wrights could not, ever, write anything but the truth as they saw it. The last lines of Wilbur's article were a tribute to Chanute's qualities, of which the whole world had long been aware, and for which the world was truly grateful:

No one was too humble to receive a share of his time. In patience and goodness of heart he has rarely been surpassed. Few men were more universally respected and loved.[4]

Although the Wrights resented the implications of the word, Chanute had indeed been their Teacher. Actually, after the publication of his book in 1894, Chanute had been The Teacher of aeronautics. In this sense he knew the joy of a teacher upon discovering the unique pupil. He saw the promise in the Wrights' work when Wilbur's first letter came to him in 1900 and for several years thereafter. He knew also the keen disappointment of the teacher when a pupil chooses another, contrary road to the one followed by his master. Chanute's relationship with the Wrights must have been the greatest joy and the greatest disappointment of his work in aeronautics. But the strongest expression of his disappointment was in his last letter to Wilbur on January 23, 1910, when he said only, "I am afraid, my friend, that your usually sound judgment has been warped by the desire for great wealth."

For six months after it had obtained the temporary injunctions against Curtiss and Paulhan, the Wright Company controlled flying in the United States. The *Scientific American,* on June 25, 1910, said editorially:

As a result of the interlocutory decree of Judges Hand and Hazel the Wright brothers have controlled flying in this country for the last six months. Unless he filed a bond with the court, no aviator who used a machine equipped with ailerons or wing warping devices, operated in conjunction with a vertical rudder could make, sell, or fly his apparatus in this country.[5]

Other legal actions had also started: Herring and Curtiss had quarreled, and they, too, had taken their differences to court.[6] Eventually Curtiss gained full control of the company. C. H. Lamson, who had built Chanute's oscillating winged glider in 1902 which was tested at Kitty Hawk, in 1910 appealed for an injunction against the Wrights for infringement of his 1901 patent.[7]

When, in June, 1910, the Wrights' temporary injunctions were vacated by a higher court, this did not settle the issue, but merely caused the legal processes to begin all over again with new trials for infringement to be started.[8] In France and in Germany the Wright patents were the subjects of long and involved litigation. Eventually there was a lawsuit in Great Britain as well. These various suits dragged on, in complicated and expensive fashion, for several years.

[3] W. Wright, on Octave Chanute, *Aeronautics* (New York), Vol. VIII, No. 1 (January, 1911), 4.

[4] *Ibid.*

[5] *Scientific American,* Vol. 102 (June 25, 1910), 514.

[6] *Aeronautics* (New York), Vol. VI, No. 2 (February, 1910), 69; *ibid.,* Vol. VI, No. 3 (March, 1910), 91.

[7] *Flight* (London), Vol. II (July 9, 1910), 527

[8] Hayward, *Aeronautical Practice, Part II,* 69; Brewer, "With the Wrights in America," *Flight* (London), Vol. II (September 3, 1910), 706.

In this country the lawsuits had effects which were not beneficial to the development of aviation. Yearbooks and magazines reported sadly and monotonously that the main progress in aviation had taken place abroad; that no international feats had been chalked up by this country.[9] Although this was an exaggeration, it approximated the truth. Military aeronautics also slumped for several years. The impetus first given by the army's purchase of the Wright plane slowed down and almost disappeared for a while.[10]

Civil aviation showed the same slump. In one tabulation of flights in 1910 and the first five months of 1911, a total of 151 flights remarkable for speed, distance, or making new records, were listed. Only the small number of 24, or 16 per cent of the 151 flights had been made in the United States. The Curtiss machines were offering serious competition to the Wrights': of the 24 flights in this same tabulation, 10 had been made in Wright planes, 10 in Curtiss planes, and 4 in Farmans. Victor Lougheed, in the third edition, 1911, of his *Vehicles of the Air,* wrote: "At the present time, however, the Wright machine does not hold a single distance, duration, speed, weight-carrying, cross-country, or altitude record in the world."[11] However, since the Wrights believed that the other planes infringed their patents, necessarily it followed that their success was due to the Wrights' methods.

The arguments pro and con the Wrights' lawsuits affected everyone interested in aviation, and the differences of opinion became so heated that aviation circles were split into two opposing camps: Curtiss and Wright, the two main companies in the country, were fighting each other in the courts; the chief schools were, for a time, run by the same two companies; each sent out exhibition teams to compete in fairs and con-

[9] American Yearbook, 1911, 1912, 1913; *Aerial Age* (New York), Vol. I, No. 10 (May 24, 1915), 221; *Aeronautics* (New York), Vol. IX, No. 1 (July, 1911), 25.

[10] U. S. House of Representatives, 70 Cong., 1 sess., *Hearings, "Pioneer Aviators,"* 5.

[11] Lougheed, *Vehicles of the Air,* 152.

234

tests; each designed planes for the army and the navy; and each taught officers in the services. The cloud of the Curtiss-Wright fight hung heavy over American aviation;[12] the arguments about it continue to this day.

For those foreign flyers who considered coming to this country to give exhibitions, the possibility of being forced to pay heavy royalties was as discouraging as a high tariff wall. There was, for example, the famous British flyer, Claude Grahame-White, who was induced to enter the Harvard Aeronautical Society Meet by its manager, the well-known flyer and inventor James V. Martin. Grahame-White electrified the United States by his spectacular flights in 1910—and collected an estimated $100,000 in the course of doing so. The Wright Company instituted suit against White for using "infringing machines"—Farman and Bleriot planes—and in 1911 was granted an injunction. The court order had these results: White had to obtain the Wrights' permission to fly in this country; if they granted it, he must either fly a Wright plane or pay royalties on any other machine that he used.[13] In addition, White had to give a financial accounting dating from November, 1910.[14]

Nevertheless, despite the threat of the heavy hand of the law, there was an enthusiastic new generation in America which wanted, more than anything else in the world, to fly. And it was willing to pay a heavy price to do so. The exhibition flyers had to pay large per cents of their (frequently large) earnings to the companies for the lawsuit funds. Planes could not be bought from these companies, but were leased out. Aero clubs that wanted to arrange for meets had to make sure first of getting the Wright Company's permission.

Early in 1910 the Aero Club of America (only official representative in the United States of the Fédération Aéro-

12 Freudenthal, *The Aviation Business*, 14–16.
13 Hayward, *Aeronautical Practice, Part II*, 80.
14 *Aircraft* (New York), Vol. II, No. 11 (January, 1912), 377.

nautique Internationale) came to an agreement with the Wrights which in effect put its power behind the company: the Aero Club of America would sanction meets and contests only if proper arrangements had first been made with the Wright Company, and the company would license promoters of meets if approved by the Aero Club. This arrangement would continue as long as the Courts upheld the validity of the Wright Company's patents. A storm of controversy arose after this agreement was announced.[15]

But the new generation gladly hurdled these and other difficulties, and, while it may not have chalked up many international records, nevertheless these young flyers expanded the achievements in this country. The United States owes a large debt to the exhibition flyers who began in 1910 to bring flying to all the corners of the country; who slowly stretched the distance records and the records for altitude; who applied the airplane to new uses; and who, in spite of the difficulties of patents and patent rights, built their own planes and started their own aviation schools.

The story of aviation was no longer the story of Wilbur and Orville Wright. It became, from now on, the story of Curtiss's first pupil, Charles F. Willard, and the Wrights' first civilian pupil in America, Walter S. Brookins; it was the story of army and navy officers—Benjamin D. Foulois, T. DeWitt Milling, T. G. Ellyson, H. C. Richardson, and Paul W. Beck; of men who added new features to the airplane and themselves flew for new records—Major Rudolph W. Schroeder, James Floyd Smith; of other inventors and designers—Charles Healy Day, Anthony Stadlman, James V. Martin, and Grover C. Loening; of men like Virginius E. Clark and Frank P. Lahm; of the men who taught others, like the De Lloyd Thompson—Max Lille school in Chicago, where Katherine

[15] Studer, *Sky Storming Yankee*, 217; Arthur W. Page, "How the Wrights Discovered Flight," *World's Work*, Vol. XX (August, 1910), 13315; *Aircraft* (New York), Vol. I, No. 4 (June, 1910), 153.

Stinson, one of the most remarkable flyers in the country, started her notable career; of other women who flew into fame, like Harriet Quimby, Mathilde Moisant, Hilder Smith, and Ruth Law; of men of the older generation like Albert F. Zahm and A. A. Merrill, who continued to work on the scientific aspects and thus became members of the new generation.

These were only a few of the many brilliant flyers, designers, and scientists who had seen the doors of the hangar swing open, and who crowded into aviation, insisting (as many of them are still doing today) on taking part in the development of this new invention.

Wilbur and Orville were not included in this new generation. Their function had been, as Chanute wrote them, the completion of the solution of a world-old problem. The commercialization of the airplane had also been their function—possibly the most important part. The legal clarification of the patent situation was their next step, and to this they devoted their energies. Increasingly they were absorbed by the lawsuits. They flew only on rare occasions; in order to test the planes that their companies were producing, or to take up famous persons as their passengers.

Once, in 1911, they returned again to Kitty Hawk. Orville made a world record there for soaring—he hovered in one spot for nine minutes and forty-five seconds.[16] This record stood for about eleven years. But there were no reporters in 1911, as there had been in 1908, hiding behind the sand dunes and fighting the mosquitoes for a glimpse of Orville in his gliders. In fact, slight attention was paid to this record even by the aeronautical magazines. In only two years the brothers had ceased to be headline news.

Actually they were experiencing the usual fate of public characters: to some, they continued to be heroes; to others, they were showing the clay feet supposedly possessed by all

[16] *Airway Age,* Vol. IX, No. 12 (December, 1928), 37; *U. S. Air Services,* Vol. VII, No. 11 (December, 1922), 7.

mankind. In short, they were admired and denigrated, worshiped and belittled; their past exploits were either exaggerated or minimized. Unfortunately, the Wrights had little liking for and less ability to carry easily the prominence to which they had risen. Fiercely and rigidly, with the same persistence which they had displayed in developing their plane, they were now determined that the world should acknowledge them as pioneers and inventors.

Wilbur once said, allegedly, that he had not married because he could not afford both a wife and an airplane. Taken as a witticism, this was emotionally true: the brothers had lived with their plane—that bounded their lives. They could not, truly, spare the energy to take on wives.

From now on the brothers were an incorporated fact: their personal histories, always identical with the fate of their aeroplane, faded into the welter of arguments, controversies, and lawsuits. The brothers were as involved with the legal complications as they had formerly been absorbed by their plane.

The Wright lawsuits did indeed affect aviation history, but they are the story of the aviation business, not the story of Wilbur and Orville Wright.

CHAPTER XIV

Orville Is Left Alone

THE LAWSUITS dragged on. Their devious progress through the courts required the personal attention of the Wright brothers and also their presence as chief witnesses. They had to travel to New York where the lawsuit against Curtiss was being heard, and also to France and to Germany. In addition, the brothers spent some time on the other phases of their business, and as always throughout their lives, they worked hard: their schools, exhibition teams, and the testing of the companies' planes, all demanded their attention.

As they neared the end of the legal battles sudden tragedy interrupted their work. Wilbur became ill early in May, 1912, and succumbed to typhoid fever. In a few days, overworked and overtired, Wilbur Wright died, on May 30, 1912.

Wilbur's sudden death left Orville alone at the age of only forty-one. What might have been the beginning of a new and fruitful life for the brothers was thus stopped short by a cruel fate. After their lawsuits were won and they were financially secure, their remarkably harmonious combination of minds might have gone on to explore the many subjects that had interested them. One can speculate endlessly about the possibilities that the future held for these devoted brothers. But it is an idle and sad inquiry, for the creative work of the Wright brothers ended with Wilbur's death in 1912.

The world appreciated this unique harmony between Orville and Wilbur, but found no way of expressing its sympathy to the lonely, bereaved brother. Trying awkwardly to articulate the shock that Wilbur's death caused to be felt, edi-

239

torial writers recounted the few facts known about him. His life had been synonymous with his work, and little else could be found to round out an emotional tribute.

One aeronautical journal was reduced to saying, in two succeeding issues, "He was a man apart, a man little understood." And again, "He was generally misunderstood; he realized this but apparently cared little what the world thought of him."[1] To which should have been added: as long as he and Orville were together.

A subtle and sympathetic description of Wilbur has recently been published. Cass Gilbert, famous architect, met him in October, 1909, and immediately dictated a memorandum giving his impressions. Gilbert caught the elusive character of the man; he appreciated his reserve, and realized his quiet, almost cynical sense of humor. Gilbert's description, which follows in part, paints a complete picture of Wilbur Wright:

His personality interested me very much. He is a man a little below average height, very slender and wiry in build. He is smooth shaven and his face is wrinkled and without much color. His eyes are a greenish blue. He occasionally looked straight at me with a very frank, clear expression but more often looked slightly to the right and downwards. He seemed to be quite unostentatious and without any pose of manner. Very simple and direct and of few words, modestly spoken. He smiled occasionally with a sort of half smile that did not give the impression of much exuberance of spirit but rather of a provincial boy who had an underlying sense of humor and perfect confidence in himself but with a slightly provincial cynicism as to how seriously the other man might regard him or his views. He was totally impassive and I should say unimpressionable so far as the surface went, but probably very keenly sensitive, and on the whole rather the type of high grade, intelligent and well read mechanic whom I occasionally meet in connection with building work. . . . He was dressed in very plain dark business clothes of indefinite color, probably grey, and wore

[1] *Aeronautics* (New York), Vol. X, Nos. 5–6 (May–June, 1912), 176; *ibid.*, Vol. XI, No. 1 (July, 1912), 1.

a derby hat throughout the conversation which only added to the general inconspicuousness of the man.

I remember distinctly that in answering my questions or replying he would look directly into my face and the sort of a wan, half-cynical but kindly smile would flit across his countenance and disappear.

There is absolutely nothing romantic or distinguished in his dress, appearance or manner.[2]

A personality such as this could not be caught by writers who had to turn out splashy obituaries. Their plight was increased by the fact that the lawsuits were not yet finally settled, and, therefore, writers did not know how to define exactly the Wrights' work. The *Scientific American* straddled the problem by describing the individual elements of the Wright machine and ascribing each to a predecessor in the art—the trussing came from Chanute, for example, and the forward horizontal rudder from Maxim—and the article ended: "Not a single element in the machine was absolutely novel; yet the machine as a whole was the most novel mechanism that could be imagined."[3]

In his work as in his life, Wilbur could not be considered as a separate entity, apart from Orville. As one journal stated movingly, "It is difficult—we have found it impossible—to write of Wilbur alone."

Although their whole work was a monument to their singleness, Wilbur's will, executed only a few weeks before he died, was the last tangible proof of their great mutual affection. In part it read as follows:

Item II. I hereby give to my father Milton Wright, of Dayton, Ohio, my earnest thanks for his example of a courageous, upright life, and for his earnest sympathy with everything tending to my true welfare; and in addition I give and bequeath to him

[2] "Notes and Documents: Cass Gilbert and Wilbur Wright," *Minnesota History*, Vol. XXII, No. 3 (September, 1941), 303–304.
[3] *Scientific American*, Vol. 106 (June 8, 1912), 518.

the sum of One Thousand Dollars ($1000.00), which I desire him to use for little unusual expeditures as might add to his comfort and pleasure.

Item III. I hereby give, will and bequeath to my oldest brother Reuchlin Wright, of Tongonoxie, Kansas, the sum of Fifty Thousand Dollars ($50,000.00), to my second brother Lorin Wright, of Dayton, Ohio, the sum of Fifty Thousand Dollars, ($50,000.00), and to my sister Katharine Wright, of Dayton, Ohio, the sum of Fifty Thousand Dollars ($50,000.00), which amounts shall be paid to them as soon as practicable after my decease.

Item IV. The entire balance and residue of my estate remaining after the satisfaction of the foregoing bequests, and be the same real, personal or mixed, and wherever situate, including interest in patents, issued or pending, inventions, contracts, and any and all holdings and interests whether specifically mentioned or not, I give, will, devise and bequeath to my brother Orville Wright, of Dayton, Ohio, who has been associated with me in all the hopes and labors both of childhood and manhood, and who, I am sure, will use the property in very much the same manner as we would use it together in case we would both survive until old age. And for this reason, I make no specific bequest to charity.

(Signed) Wilbur Wright.
Dated May 10, 1912.[4]

According to a contemporary account, Orville received under this will something over $126,000, which represented about half of the profits made by the brothers up to this time.[5]

[4] *Aero and Hydro,* Vol. V (October 26, 1912), 59.
[5] *Ibid.*

CHAPTER XV

Pyrrhic Victories

ORVILLE LIVED WITH Katharine in the new house in Dayton. For several years after Wilbur's death, he made a brave attempt to carry on a role in aviation. In 1913 he received the Collier Trophy for his automatic stability device. He read a paper before the Franklin Society in Philadelphia,[1] which was accorded the honor of being reprinted in the Smithsonian Institution's annual report for 1914—the second and last time that the brothers were given this scientific recognition. He served on various aeronautical bodies, such as the National Advisory Committee for Aeronautics, the Daniel Guggenheim Fund for the Promotion of Aeronautics, and the National Aeronautic Association. Like many early flyers, he flew rarely as the years passed; by 1914, and again in 1916, it was news when Orville occasionally flew. The last time he piloted a plane was in 1918, flying an early biplane alongside a new DH-4.[2]

Orville continued with the lawsuits as they dragged on. They were settled in 1917, although in 1914, the Wright companies had won technical victories. But these were victories that Orville had to enjoy alone. He had become president of the (American) Wright Company after Wilbur's death. In 1915 his large stock interest was purchased by a syndicate headed by William Boyce Thompson. Orville was retained by the new corporation as "chief aeronautical engineer, at a large

[1] Orville Wright, "Stability of Aeroplanes," *Journal* of the Franklin Institute (Philadelphia), Vol. 178, No. 3 (1914), 249–58.

[2] *The New York Times*, December 17, 1933.

salary, will be in charge of the laboratory at Dayton" according to the new vice-president, C. S. Jennison.[3]

This interview continued with an apology for the lawsuits. Answering the criticisms that had been made through the years, Jennison said, "It has been said that he [Orville] was too selfish with his patents for the good of aviation. This was unjust. Mr. Wright became involved soon after the formation of his company in 1909 in a number of infringement suits, with the result that he was forced to give more of his time to protecting the patents than to promoting their use. Now, however, this will no longer be the case. We will take care of everything. Mr. Wright will continue his life's work."[4]

Actually, Orville had retired. He was reported as saying, once again, that he intended to devote his time to scientific work.[5] But his creative energies had suffered a mortal blow, and his role became a passive one. During the first World War, in 1915, the (English) *Daily Mail* suggested that he be placed in charge of British aviation. Orville would not discuss this idea, and it was never revealed whether he had actually received an offer from England. Since nothing came of it, the press suggested that he had refused an alleged offer because of his father's pacifism, and his own aversion to war. Others brought forth the suggestion that Orville's poor health was the basis for a refusal. Increasingly the rumors grew that his health had been impaired in 1908 by the accident at Fort Myer.

Orville himself, in 1934, gave his health as the grounds for refusing to serve on a committee appointed to investigate the army's carrying of the air mail after the contracts of the private companies had been canceled.[6] He thereby missed a fine opportunity to point out that the Army Air Force had made a

[3] *Aerial Age*, Vol. II (October 25, 1915), 130.

[4] *Ibid.*

[5] Fred C. Kelly, "Flying Machines and the War: An Interview with Orville Wright," *Collier's*, Vol. 55 (July 31, 1915), 25; *Scientific American*, Vol. CXI (July 18, 1914), 39.

[6] *The New York Times*, March 14, 1934; *ibid.*, March 15, 1934.

heroic attempt to carry out a hasty order, in spite of its in-
adequate funds, training facilities, and equipment.

Only occasionally did Orville appear in public. He emerged
from his jealously guarded privacy only on historical occasions
commemorating the past. He sprang into headlines when de-
fending his and Wilbur's early accomplishments and to make
attempts to establish their work as *scientists*. He avoided current issues and current activities, with the exception of the
famous and long-drawn-out argument with the Smithsonian
Institution.

That argument was also based on his firm intention to
establish the scientific priority of the Wright brothers. When
Orville, in 1928, shipped the repaired 1903 Wright plane to
the South Kensington Museum in London, that gesture was
merely the climax of long years during which the Wrights
had believed that their work had not been accorded the scientific recognition it deserved in their own country. The seeds
of this dissatisfaction went back to their first decision to strike
out on lines other than those pursued by Langley; it was increased by their conclusion in 1901 that Langley's work in
aerodynamics had been inaccurate. Orville expressed their
feeling publicly during this controversy when he wrote, years
later, of "our entire lack of confidence in Langley's scientific
work in aerodynamics."[7]

Their feeling of superiority over Langley's work was reinforced by the apparent failure in 1903 of Langley's full-sized
aerodrome and their own successful flights a few days later.
This was a victory over the "Washington group," as they
called it. Then official Washington offended the brothers,
when the War Department in 1905 first refused to buy their
plane, and they spent the following years in efforts to sell it to
foreign governments.

[7] U. S. House of Representatives, 70 Cong., 1 sess., Military Affairs Committee,
Subcommittee No. 8, *Hearings,* "First Heavier-than-Air Machine," (April 27,
1928), 26.

In 1914, the Smithsonian sponsored tests of Langley's reconstructed aerodrome, but it unfortunately accepted Glenn H. Curtiss's offer to make the tests at Hammondsport. This brought the Wrights' chief rival into direct opposition to them immediately after the Wrights had won a legal victory over Curtiss. In addition, the Smithsonian Institution chose the well-known aeronautical scientist, Albert F. Zahm, to be the observer at the Hammonsport tests—and Zahm was Curtiss's expert witness during the lawsuits!

The final gesture which offended Orville was the exhibition of the reconstructed Langley aerodrome with a label saying that this was "the first man-carrying aeroplane in the history of the world capable of sustained free flight." After some controversy, the label was changed in 1925 by preceding the above words with the phrase, "In the opinion of many competent to judge. . . ." A paragraph was added, stating that the Wrights' plane had made the first free flight in the world under its own power.[8]

Nevertheless, Orville continued to feel injured. He took to his pen and wrote long letters charging in detail the various structural changes that had been made in Langley's aerodrome for the 1914 tests. In the midst of this controversy, Herring's voice was heard once more. Neglected and forgotten, in bad health and poverty-stricken, Herring asked that a Congressional investigation be made to determine the real history of the airplane.

The Smithsonian Institution made a final change of the label for the Langley aerodrome, saying only: "The original Langley flying machine of 1903, restored."

This did not satisfy Orville. The Wright plane was sent to London.

---

[8] Abbot, "The Relations Between the Smithsonian Institution and the Wright Brothers," Smithsonian *Miscellaneous Collections*, Vol. 81, No. 5 (September 29, 1928), 10; "The 1914 Tests of the Langley Aerodrome," Smithsonian *Miscellaneous Collections*, Vol. 103, No. 8 (1942).

In 1942 the Smithsonian apologized officially for the seeming slights of the Wright brothers' claims during this long quarrel. In a public statement it was granted that Langley's aerodrome had been altered in 1914, and that, therefore, the tests had not proved whether or not it might have flown in 1903. The following year marked the fortieth anniversary of the Wrights' first flights in 1903. In celebration of this date, on December 17, 1943, President Franklin D. Roosevelt made the announcement that the repaired 1903 plane was being returned to this country after the war.

Nothing definite was heard of the matter until Orville's death in January, 1948—and then the issue was not clearly settled. For Orville's will bequeathed the plane to the Kensington Museum in England. But a letter written in 1943, six years after the date of the will, asked that the plane be returned to the United States at some later time, when the war would be over.[9] Not long after Orville's will was made public, the South Kensington Museum courteously made arrangements to return the plane to this country. Here, Dr. Paul E. Garber of the Smithsonian's National Air Museum made ready to welcome it. It arrived in time for the forty-fifth anniversary of its famous flights on December 17, 1903. Both brothers having died, the affection of the country centered on the plane and followed its careful progress across the ocean, guarded by Dr. Herman Shaw of the London Museum. The little plane, tucked into a crate for safekeeping, received the accumulated interest of forty-five years.

The Smithsonian Institution placed a label on the aeroplane which reads:

[9] Some confusion was added to the situation by the following statement by Griffith Brewer, old friend of the Wrights: "Orville Wright . . . decided to accept a proposal previously made by the Science Museum in London that he should lend the original Wright machine for exhibition in the Science Museum for a period of five years, *or until it was withdrawn by Orville personally*. In return the Science Museum undertook to house and exhibit the machine *for all time unless withdrawn after the first five years* by Orville Wright." Brewer, *Fifty Years of Flying,* 112. The italics are mine.

THE ORIGINAL WRIGHT BROTHERS' AEROPLANE

The world's first power-driven heavier-than-air Machine in which man made free, controlled, and sustained flight.

Invented and built by Wilbur and Orville Wright, flown by them at Kitty Hawk, North Carolina, December 17, 1903.

By original scientific research the Wright Brothers discovered the principles of human flight. As inventors, builders, and flyers they further developed the aeroplane, taught man to fly, and opened the era of aviation.

Deposited by the Estate of Orville Wright.

The honored place of the Wright brothers in the long history of aeronautics would seem to be little affected by the final resting place of the repaired 1903 plane and less so by the labels finally decided upon. As long as history is written, both Langley and the Wrights will occupy foremost places in the story of flying. There are infinite numbers of solutions to any one problem, and no solution is ever the final one, or the only one. And so each contributor in the long procession of those who developed aeronautics has his unique place of honor.

While the exact words in which to describe the exact contribution of Langley and of the Wright brothers will always be matters for discussion, it is indubitable, and more pertinent, to remember that all were of vital importance in the development of flying.

As to the lawsuits and quarrels about priority of ideas, all inventions are matters of growth: to apply another's ideas and to expand them are a tribute to the ideas. And who can weigh mathematically the importance of a thought? As the history of the Wrights' work starts before they began—in fact, before they were born—so the influence of their achievements stretches far into the future, and will last as long as men live and fly.

Orville lived out a long and lonely life. His father died in 1917, five years after Wilbur. In 1920, Reuchlin, another brother, died. At the end of 1926 Katharine left him, to marry Henry J. Haskell, editor of the *Kansas City Star*.

Daytonians split into two groups about Orville, as aviation circles have always been split pro and con the Wrights. One faction insisted that he was a gentle, shy, elderly man (he was born in 1871) who suffered constantly from his old injuries. The other group believed him to be so eccentric that he resented Katharine's marriage because it left him alone, and that he refused to attend her funeral in 1929 (when she died of pneumonia) because he could not forgive her for abandoning him. The fact is that Katharine was buried in Dayton, next to Wilbur.[10]

The Wrights' motives were always obscured by the sensitiveness, shyness, and complexity of their personalities. To his death, Orville continued to keep secret his personal life and to live in great seclusion. Wilbur had never made many speeches, but they were, nevertheless, more frequent than Orville's. On the rare occasions when Orville appeared in public in the years after Wilbur's death, he avoided making speeches when possible, even though those occasions were generally memorials to the Wrights' past achievements.

Orville was entirely alone, after his brother Lorin died in 1939. He was the last of his generation.

In the last years of his life he became almost a legend, indistinguishable from Wilbur to the younger generation. Surely this did not disturb, and was, rather, the choice of this modest and quiet man whose heart had died in 1912, although he himself lived on until January 30, 1948. Then, after only a few days' illness, Orville died at the age of seventy-seven.[11]

Orville Wright's emphasis on the early years of their work

[10] Brewer, *Fifty Years of Flying*, 115.

[11] Orville Wright's estate of $1,067,105 was left largely to Oberlin College, Ohio (from which his sister Katharine graduated), to Berea College, Kentucky, and to his nieces and nephews.

was correct. Their contribution was made in the ten years from 1900 to 1910.

It began with Wilbur's first letter to Chanute, early in 1900, describing their hopes and plans tentatively and half-humorously. Then came their active experiments and the success of their 1902 glider, which embodied their famous method of control. This was followed by their first success on that stormy day in 1903 when they made their first brief flights in a powered plane. By 1905 they had flown a distance of over twenty-four miles while other men were still trying to fly a few hundred yards, and they had mastered the art of circling. They had modified their plane so as to eliminate the disturbing undulations, and it was in its final form.

After several years of effort to find a market for their product, they had two brief years of great popular acclaim, in 1908 and 1909, when their flying was superior to any other in the world, and they were the unconquered kings of the air.

The later quarrels have too long obscured the real work of the Wrights. The overpublicized lawsuits and arguments were, unfortunately, attempts to force the world to an acknowledgment that the brothers, and they alone, had been the first in the world to fly; that they were *the* inventors of the aeroplane; that the world owed its first aeroplane to them. Actually, their contribution was sufficient to place them high among the great men of the world without attempting to exclude the work of prior inventors. Moreover, their feats in themselves building their own gliders, engines, and planes, and in making the controlled, sustained flights in 1903 at Kitty Hawk, were indeed achievements in America and by Americans. What they did was sufficient in itself without begrudging to men of their own and other nationalities their contributions in this first decade of flight.

By their flights the Wright brothers dominated the first era of flying. There is little need to quarrel about labels and tags when the influence of these two men was so great that it started hundreds of young people on the road to flying and to fame. When the Wrights stopped public flying, in 1910, their work had been done. Their story ends, actually, with their amazing flights as the premier pilots of the world, when they showed two continents their mastery: Wilbur in France, and Orville at Fort Myer; Wilbur in Italy, and Orville in Germany; and Wilbur circling the Statue of Liberty. The fade-out should be the Wrights' triumphant return to their own country in 1909, and its wildly enthusiastic reception to them; with a picture of President Taft presenting them with the gold medals from the Congress of the United States.

They had made good business arrangements by 1910; they had won their real battle, for they had proved that flights could be made and controlled and extended; their planes, at that moment, were the most successful in the world. They had really pushed open the doors of the hangar. The airplane was ready for the other men and women who would conquer a new dimension.

The last picture should be not the lawsuits and quarrels about labels but the return of Wilbur and Orville Wright to their beloved city as its foremost citizens to receive its homage. In the background of this triumphant return and sharing in their success as they had contributed to it, are their beloved sister Katharine and their precursor and friend, Octave Chanute.

Abbott, Charles G. "The Relations Between the Smithsonian Institution and the Wright Brothers," Smithsonian Institution *Miscellaneous Collections,* Vol. 81, No. 5 (September 29, 1928), Publication No. 2977.

———. "The 1914 Tests of the Langley Aerodrome," Smithsonian Institution *Miscellaneous Collections,* Vol. 103, No. 8 (1942).

Adams, Heinrich. *Flug von Heinrich Adams—Unser Flieger von Wilbur und Orville Wright.* Leipzig, C. F. Amelangs Verlag, 1909. (The article by the Wright brothers is a translation of "The Wright Brothers' Aeroplane," *q.v.*)

Aero Club of America. *Navigating the Air.* New York, Doubleday, Page and Company, 1907.

Almanach des Aviateurs pour 1909. Paris, A. Mericant, Ed., 1909.

American Yearbook for 1910, 1911, and 1912. New York, D. Appleton and Company, 1911, 1912, 1913.

Armengaud, J., jeune. *Le Problème de L'Aviation: Sa Solution par L'Aéroplane.* Paris, Librairie Ch. Delagrave, 1908. Third edition.

Bell, Alexander Graham. "Aerial Locomotion," Washington Academy of Sciences, *Proceedings,* Vol. VIII, 1906–1907 (March 4, 1907).

Bia, Georges. *Les Frères Wright et Leur Oeuvre—Rapport Présenté à la Section Aéronautique de la Société Belge des Ingénieurs et des Industriels.* Paris, Librairie des Sciences Aéronautique, F.-Louis Vivien, 1910.

Brewer, Griffith. *Fifty Years of Flying.* London, Air League of the British Empire, 1946.

———. "The Life and Work of Wilbur Wright," *The Aeronautical Journal* (London), Vol. XX, No. 79 (July–September, 1916). This basic work includes the following appendices, which are also of great importance:

Appendix A: Extracts from Wilbur Wright, *Snap-Shots* (November 17, 1894).

Appendix B: Reprint of Wilbur Wright, "Some Aeronautical Experiments," *q.v.*

Appendix C: Letter of December 6, 1905, from Harvey M. Weaver to Frank Lahm, which was read by Lahm on December 29, 1905, before the Aviation Committee of the Aéro Club de France.

Appendix D: Reprint of Wright brothers, "The Wright Brothers' Aeroplane," *q.v.*

Appendix E: Reprint of Wilbur Wright, "What Mouillard Did," Aero Club of America *Bulletin,* Vol. 1 (April, 1912).

Appendix F: Reprint of Wilbur Wright, "What Clement Ader Did," Aero Club of America *Bulletin,* Vol. I (May, 1912).

Appendix G: Testimony of Wilbur Wright on February 15, 1912, in U. S. patent suit. This is a partial reprint from U. S. Circuit Court, Western District of New York, Wright *vs.* Herring-Curtiss, Vol. I, 474–99.

Appendix H: Letter from Wright, November 17, 1905, reprinted from *The Aeronautical Journal* (London), Vol. X (January, 1906).

Appendix I: Editorial reprinted from *The Aeronautical Journal* (London), Vol. X (April, 1906).

Appendix J: Hiram Maxim, "The Recent Experiments Conducted by the Wright Brothers," reprinted from *The Aeronautical Journal* (London), Vol. X (July, 1906).

Appendix K: Brewer, "Wilbur Wright, Gold Medallist of the Society," reprinted from *The Aeronautical Journal* (London), Vol. XVI (July, 1912).

———. "With the Wrights in America," *Flight* (London), Vol. II (September 3, 1910).

Brigole, A. *Santos-Dumont: o Pioneiro do Ar.* Rio de Janeiro, Aero Club de Brasil, 1941.

Bruce, Eric Stuart. "The Aeroplane Experiments of M. Santos-Dumont," *The Aeronautical Journal* (London), Vol. XI (January, 1907).

Casson, Herbert N. "At Last We Can Fly. The Story of the Wright Brothers, Who, After Years of Experimenting, Believe That

They Have At Last Discovered the Elusive Secret of Flight," *Pearson's Magazine* (London), Vol. XXIV (July, 1907). Also in *American Magazine,* Vol. 63 (April, 1907).

Chanute, Octave. An invaluable source for the student of aeronautics is the large collection of Chanute's correspondence, his clippings from newspapers and magazines, and his other files which are in the Library of Congress, placed there by Chanute's daughters at his express wish.

——. *Progress in Flying Machines.* New York, M. N. Forney, 1894.

——. "Aerial Navigation: Balloons and Flying Machines from the Engineering Standpoint," *Cassier's Magazine,* Vol. XX, No. 2 (June, 1901).

——. "Artificial Flight," Part III, *Pocket-Book of Aeronautics,* compiled by Hermann W. L. Moedebeck, *q.v.*

——. "Chronology of Aviation," Smithsonian Institution *Annual Report,* 1910.

——. "Experiments in Flying: An Account of the Author's Own Inventions and Adventures," *McClure's Magazine,* Vol. XV, No. 2 (June, 1902).

——. "First Steps in Aviation and Memorable Flights," *Aeronautics* (New York), Vol. IV, No. 1 (January, 1909).

——. "Gliding Experiments," *Journal* of the Western Society of Engineers, Vol. II, No. 5 (October, 1897).

——. "A History of the Wright Flying Experiments," *Scientific American,* Vol. 63 (June 1, 1907), Supplement No. 1639.

——. "Langley, *son Vie et son Oeuvre,*" *L'Aérophile* (Paris), année XIV (April, 1906).

——. "Recent Aeronautical Progress in the United States," *The Aeronautical Journal* (London), Vol. XII, No. 47 (July, 1908).

——. "Recent Progress in Aviation," Smithsonian Institution *Annual Report,* 1910; reprinted from *Journal* of the Western Society of Engineers, Vol. XV (April, 1910).

——. "Sailing Flight," *Aeronautical Annual* (Boston), Nos. 2 and 3 (1896–97).

da Foncesca, Gondin. *Santos Dumont.* Rio de Janeiro, Casa Editoria Vecchi, ltda., cor. e aumentada, 1940. Second edition.

Dame, Lawrence. *New England Comes Back*. New York, Random House, 1940.

Dictionary of American Biography, Vol. IV. New York, Charles Scribner's Sons, 1930.

Dienstbach, Carl. "Herring's Work," *American Aeronaut and Aerostatist,* Vol. I, No. 7 (May, 1908).

———. "The Revelations at Fort Myer," *American Aeronaut,* Vol. I, No. 2 (September, 1909).

———. "Introduction," *Navigating the Air,* Aero Club of America.

Ferber, Ferdinand. *L'Aviation: Ses Débuts—Son Développement—De Crête à Crête—De Ville à Ville—De Continent à Continent.* Paris et Nancy, Berger-Levrault et Cie, Ed., 1908; fifth edition, 1909. (Second edition translated into German: *Die Kunst zu Fliegen: Ihre Anfänge—ihre Entwicklung.* Berlin, Richard Carl Schmidt, 1910.)

Flint, Charles R. *Memories of an Active Life.* New York, G. P. Putnam's Sons, 1923.

Freudenthal, Elsbeth E. *The Aviation Business: From Kitty Hawk to Wall Street.* New York, The Vanguard Press, 1940.

Guggenheim, Daniel, Medal for Achievements in Aeronautics, New York, 1932.

Hayward, Charles B. *Aeronautical Practice,* Part II: Instruction Paper. Chicago, American School of Correspondence, 1912.

———. *Practical Aeronautics,* with an Introduction by Orville Wright. Chicago, American School of Correspondence, 1912.

Henderson, Archibald. *Contemporary Immortals.* New York, D. Appleton and Company, 1930.

Hildebrandt, Alfred L. H. *Die Brüder Wright: Eine Studie über die Entwicklung der Flugmachine von Lilienthal bis Wright.* Berlin, Otto Elsner Verlagsges., 1909.

Johnston, S. Paul. *Horizons Unlimited: A Graphic History of Aviation.* New York, Duell, Sloane and Pearce, 1941.

Kelly, Fred C. *The Wright Brothers: A Biography Authorized by Orville Wright.* New York, Harcourt, Brace and Company, 1943.

———. "Flying Machines and the War: An Interview with Orville Wright," *Collier's,* Vol. 55 (July 31, 1915).

————. "How the Wright Brothers Began," *Harper's Magazine,* Vol. 179 (October, 1939).

Langley, Samuel Pierpont. "Experiments with the Langley Aerodrome," Smithsonian Institution *Annual Report,* 1903–1904.

Lougheed, Victor. *Vehicles of the Air: A Popular Exposition of Modern Aeronautics with Working Drawings.* Chicago, The Reilly and Britton Company, 1909; third edition, 1911.

Maitland, Lester J. *Knights of the Air.* New York, Doubleday, Doran and Company, 1929.

Manly, Charles M. "Discussion" of Alexander Graham Bell's paper, Washington Academy of Sciences, *Proceedings,* Vol. VIII, 1906–1907 (March 4, 1907).

Martin, James V. "When Will Merit Count in Aviation?" *The Libertarian* (Greenville, S. C.), Vol. III, No. 4 (October, 1924).

Maxim, Hiram S. *Artificial and Natural Flight.* London, Whittaker and Company, 1908; second edition, 1909.

Moedebeck, Hermann W. L. In collaboration with O. Chanute and Others. *Pocket-Book of Aeronautics.* London, Whittaker and Company, 1907.

————. *Fliegende Menschen.* Berlin, Verlag von Otto Salle, 1909.

Newton, Byron R. "Recollections of the Days When Wings Emerged," *U. S. Air Services,* Vol. 17 (January, 1932).

Page, Arthur W. "How the Wrights Discovered Flight," *World's Work,* Vol. XX (August, 1910).

Peyrey, François. *Les Oiseaux Artificiels: Avec un Préface de Santos-Dumont.* Paris, H. Dunod et E. Pinat, 1909.

————. *L'Oeuvre de l'Aéro-Club de France et L'Aéronautique Contemporaine.* Paris, 1909.

————. *Les Premiers Hommes-Oiseaux: Wilbur et Orville Wright.* Paris, 1908.

Planck, Charles E. *Women with Wings.* New York, Harper and Brothers, 1942.

Randers-Pehrson, N. H. "Pioneer Wind Tunnels," Smithsonian Institution *Miscellaneous Collections,* Vol. 93, No. 4 (January 19, 1935), Publication No. 3294.

Rotch, A. Lawrence. *The Conquest of the Air, or the Advent of Aerial Navigation.* New York, Moffat, Yard and Company, 1909.

Sahel, Jacques. *Henry Farman et L'Aviation*. Paris, Ed. Bernard Grosset, 1936.

Salmonsen's *Konversationslexikon,* Vol VII. Copenhagen, 1918

Santos-Dumont, Alberto. *My Air-ships*. New York, The Century Company, 1904.

South Kensington Museum (London). *Handbook of the Collections Illustrating Aeronautics,* 1929–34, parts 1–3.

Squier, George O. "The Present Status of Military Aeronautics," *The Journal* of the American Society of Mechanical Engineers, Vol. XXX (December, 1908).

———. "The Wright Brothers—A Bit of History," *Flight* (London), Vol. V (June 14, 1913).

Studer, Clara. *Sky Storming Yankee: The Life of Glenn Curtiss*. New York, Stackpole Sons, 1937.

Sullivan, Mark. *Our Times: The United States, 1900–1925*. Vol. II, *America Finding Herself*. New York, Charles Scribner's Sons, 1927.

Turner, George Kibbe. "The Men Who Learned to Fly. The Wright Brothers' Story of Their Experiments, the Sensations of Flight, and Their Estimate of the Future of the Aeroplane," *McClure's Magazine,* Vol. XXX, No. 4 (February, 1908).

U. S. Circuit Court for the Western District of New York. Orville and Wilbur Wright *vs.* Herring-Curtiss Co. and Glenn H. Curtiss. In Equity No. 400.

U. S. Circuit Court of Appeals, 2nd Circuit. Wright Co. *vs.* Herring-Curtiss Co. and Glenn H. Curtiss.

U. S. Circuit Court of Appeals. 2nd Circuit. Wright Co. *vs.* Louis Paulhan.

U. S. House of Representatives, 70 Cong., 1 sess., Military Affairs Committee, *Hearings* on H. Res. 11273, "Pioneer Aviators," April 3, 1928.

U. S. House of Representatives, 70 Cong., 1 sess., Military Affairs Committee, Subcommittee No. 8, *Hearings,* "First heavier-than-air Flying Machine," April 27, 1928.

U. S. House of Representatives, 74 Cong., 1 sess., Committee on Patents, *Hearings,* "Pooling of Patents," February 11, 14, 20, 25, 28, March 7, 1935.

Voisin, Gabriel. *La Naissance de l'Aéroplane*. Paris, Librairies Hachette, 1928.

Webb, M. G. and E. L. *Famous Living Americans*. Greencastle, Ind., Charles Webb and Company, 1915.

Wright, Orville. "How We Made the First Flight," *Flying* (New York), Vol. II, No. 11 (December, 1913).

———. "Our Early Flying Machine Developments," *The Slipstream* (Dayton, O.), Vol. VIII, No. 9 (September, 1927).

———. "Stability of Aeroplanes," *Journal* of the Franklin Institute (Philadelphia), Vol. 178 (1914).

Wright, Wilbur. "The Earliest Wright Flights—A Letter from Wilbur Wright," *Scientific American*, Vol. 103 (July 16, 1910).

———. "Experiments and Observations in Soaring Flight," *Journal* of the Western Society of Engineers, Vol. VIII, No. 4 (August, 1903).

———. "Flying as a Sport—Its Possibilities," *Scientific American*, Vol. 98 (February 29, 1908).

———. "Some Aeronautical Experiments," *Journal* of the Western Society of Engineers, Vol. VI, No. 6 (December, 1901).

———. "What Clement Ader Did," Aero Club of America *Bulletin*, Vol. I (May, 1912).

———. "What Mouillard Did," Aero Club of America *Bulletin*, Vol. I (April, 1912).

———. "Otto Lilienthal," Aero Club of America *Bulletin*, Vol I (September, 1912).

———. On Octave Chanute (no title) in *Aeronautics* (New York), Vol. VIII, No. 1 (January, 1911).

Wright brothers. "Our Aeroplane Tests at Kitty Hawk," *Scientific American*, Vol. 98 (June 13, 1908).

———. "The Relation of Weight, Speed, and Power of Flyers," in *Navigating the Air*, Aero Club of America, *q.v.*

———. "The Wright Brothers' Aeroplane," *Century Magazine*, Vol. LXXVI, No. 5 (September, 1908).

———. Communication to the Aero Club of America, *Scientific American*, Vol. 61 (April 7, 1906), Supplement No. 1579.

———. Letter to the Editor, *L'Aérophile* (Paris), année XII (December, 1905).

———. Letter to the Editor, *Scientific American,* Vol. 106 (March 30, 1912).

———. Letter to Frank S. Lahm, January 3, 1906, *L'Aérophile* (Paris), année XIV (January, 1906).

———. Statement: *The Aeronautical Journal* (London), Vol. VII (April, 1904); *L'Aérophile* (Paris), année XII (January, 1904); Ferber, *L'Aviation; Chicago Daily News,* January 6, 1904.

Zahm, Albert Francis. *Aerial Navigation: A Popular Treatise on the Growth of Air Craft [sic] and on Aeronautical Meteorology.* New York, D. Appleton and Company, 1911.

———. "Octave Chanute—His Work and Influence in Aeronautics," *Scientific American,* Vol. 104, No. 19 (May 13, 1911).

This list is a selective one, for Chanute, Zahm, and others cited briefly above contributed constantly to the early literature of aeronautics. The Wright brothers' comparatively few articles were reprinted frequently in journals and books all over the world, and they themselves augmented their writings by occasional letters to magazines and individuals which, again, were reprinted widely.

Specific information on the literature can be found in the following important bibliographies:

Brockett, Paul. *Bibliography of Aeronautics.* Smithsonian Institution *Miscellaneous Collections,* Vol. 55 (1910), Publication No. 1920.

Gamble, William B. *History of Aeronautics: A Selected List of References to Material in The New York Public Library.* New York, The New York Public Library, 1938.

U. S. National Advisory Committee for Aeronautics. *Bibliography of Aeronautics,* 1909–31. Washington, Government Printing Office, 1921–35. 12 vols.

Magazines of this early period are invaluable sources of information, and particular mention must be made of the following periodicals:

L'Aérophile (Paris)
The Aeronautical Journal (London)
Aeronautics (London)
Aeronautics (New York)

Bibliography

Aerial Age (New York)

Aero and Hydro (New York)

Automotor Journal (London)—successor to the *Automotor and Horseless Vehicle Journal.*

Aviation (New York)

Flight (London)

Illustrierte Aeronautische Mitteilungen (Strassburg, and later, Berlin.)

Scientific American (New York)

Index

Flint and Company: 152, 154–55
Flugmaschine Wright, GmbH: 215
Fordyce, Arnold: 134, 135, 137
Foster, H.: 133
Foulois, Benjamin D.: 214, 236
France, aeronautical activity in: 1903, 67; 1904, 94–96; 1905, 111, 126; 1906, 142–43; 1907, 161–62, 166–68; 1908, 173–74, 177, 187, 192–93; 1909, 204–205, 210–13
Franklin, Benjamin: 106
Franklin Society: 243
Franz Josef, emperor of Austria: 136
Freedman, Andrew: 218
French commercial syndicates: 135–37, 164, 180–81, 195
French patents: Penaud and Gauchot, *vi;* Wright, 75, 96, 106, 181, 233
French War Department: 123–24, 135–36, 164

Garber, Paul E.: 247
Gastambide, Robert: 68
German patents, Wright: 68–69, 75, 106, 141, 215, 233
Germany: 120, 124, 125, 139, 142
Goodyear Company: 188 n.
Gilbert, Cass: 240
Gilmore, Lyman, Jr.: 19
Gliders and gliding: 19, 61, 65, 69, 93, 95, 112–13, 168; Lilienthal, 10, 11, 15, 24, 30, 34; Chanute, 12, 13, 18, 26–27, 32, 47, 51, 54 ff., 65; Wright, 16, 17, 18, 22–24, 30, 34, 50, 55 ff., 69, 78
Gould, Howard: 218
Grahame-White, Claude: 235
Guggenheim, Daniel, Fund for the Promotion of Aeronautics: 243

Hargrave, Lawrence: *vi,* 48, 69
Harvard Aeronautical Society Meet: 235
Haskell, Henry J.: 249
Helicopters: 10, 143, 147, 162
Henson, William S.: 55
Herring, Augustus M.: 13, 175, 194, 217, 246; first-to-fly claims, *v,* 53, 93–94, 155, 219; descriptions of, 53, 93, 175–76; *see also* lawsuits

Herring-Curtiss Company: 217, 218, 220, 223
Hersey, Henry B.: 157
Hildebrandt, Alfred L. H.: 125, 176
Hollands, Sidney H.: 48
Hovering: 78, 237
Hudson-Fulton Celebration, New York: 216–17
Huffaker, E. C.: 32, 33, 62
Huffman, Torrence: 98
Huffman Prairie: 98, 114
Humphries, Frederic E.: 217
Hydroplanes: 162, 166

International Aviation Meet (Los Angeles): 209–10, 220
International Aviation Meet (Reims): 215
International Conference on Aerial Navigation (Chicago): 19
Issy, France: 162
Italy: 139, 203; Wright patent in, 96

Japan: 139
James Gordon Bennett Trophy: 215
Jennison, C. S.: 243
Jones, Ernest LaRue: 160
June Bug: 182

Kimball, Charles: 209
Kites: *vi,* 10, 51, 168
Kitty Hawk, North Carolina: Wrights' first visit, 22; in 1901, 30–35; in 1902, 53–61; in 1903, 78–84; in 1908, 178–180; in 1911, 237
Kress, Wilhelm: 110–11
Krupp: 215

Lahm, Frank P.: 157, 188, 214, 217, 236
Lahm, Frank S.: 124, 131, 132, 136, 157
Lake, Simon: 163
Lambert, Charles de: 203, 204
Lamson, C. H.: 51, 233
Langley, Samuel Pierpont: 11–12, 14, 62–63, 73, 77, 126, 134; powered models, *vi,* 19, 37; machine, 76–77, 79, 80, 196, 246; and U. S. War Department, 76, 119, 120,

Willard, Charles F.: 209, 236
Williamson, Pliny W.: 218
Wind tunnels: 39–41
Witteman brothers: 209
World War I: 120
Wright, Katharine: 6, 163–64, 190, 205, 242, 249
Wright, Lorin: 6, 242, 249
Wright, Milton: 5–6, 7, 241, 244, 248; and church, 52, 54, 61, 98, 114
Wright, Orville: 9, 247, 249; education, 6, 7; and 1903 plane, 83 n., 245 ff.; in Europe, 168, 172, 202, 215; flights, 187–89, 212, 214–16, 237, 243; accident, 189–91, 193, 244; descriptions of, 190–91, 212; after Wilbur's death, 243 ff.; *see also* Wright brothers
Wright, Reuchlin: 6, 242, 248–49
Wright, Susan Catherine Koerner: 5
Wright, Wilbur: 6, 7, 239; health, 9, 205, 221; descriptions of, 35, 164, 165, 183–84, 186, 187, 200, 202, 240–41; in Europe, 163 ff., 180, 183 ff., 190 ff., 195, 203 ff.; flights, 185–86, 191–92, 201, 216 ff.; will, 241–42; *see also* Wright brothers
Wright brothers: flights, *vi, vii,* 81–84, 102–106, 114–16, 177–80; starting aviation business, *vi, viii,* 46, 90, 109–10, 117, 152, 223, 238; personality, 6–7, 20, 33, 43, 57–58, 70–71, 81, 89–90; and the press, 7–8, 77, 84, 86–88, 98–100, 116, 178–79; bicycle business, 9, 21–22, 29, 44–46, 47, 89, 91; propellers, 10, 72–73,

79, 190; flying as a hobby, 14, 17, 20, 44; gliders and gliding, 16, 17, 18, 22–24, 29, 30, 34, 50, 55 ff., 69, 78; control method and wing-warping, 18, 24, 55–56, 59–60, 74–76, 112, 141, 224; at Kitty Hawk, 22, 30, 54 ff., 78–84, 178–80, 237; position of operator in flight, 23, 24, 115, 167, 179; secrecy, 24–25, 49–50, 71, 85–86, 88–89, 91, 96–97, 103–104, 113, 126, 134, 140–41, 158, 173; unity of, 25, 29, 30, 239–42; scientific debt to Chanute, 26–27, 37, 92, 197–99, 228–29; patents, U. S., 32–33, 63, 73, 96, 141, 154–55, 182–83, 218 ff., 230, 244; German, 68–69, 75, 96, 106, 141, 215, 233; French, 75, 96, 106, 181, 233; British, 75, 96, 106, 205, 233; planes, 1903, 63, 73, 83, 245–48; 1904, 98, 104; 1905, 115; 1907, 167; 1908, 179; 1909, 213; later, 234; engines, 64–65, 71, 72, 146, 167; descriptions of, 66, 76, 90, 109, 178–79, 202, 219–20; and U. S. War Department, 119–21, 160–61, 169–72, 175–76, 193, 206, 211, 214–15; plane prices and contract terms, 119, 123, 125, 133, 134, 137, 153–54, 160, 167, 176, 180–81, 215–16, 219, 227; and lawsuits, 226, 237 ff.; *see also* lawsuits
Wright Company: 218, 223, 233, 235, 236, 243

Zahm, Albert Francis: 19, 40, 60, 152, 237, 246
Zeppelin: 120